EVOLUTION ON TRIAL

By
CORA A. RENO

MOODY PRESS
CHICAGO

Printed in the United States of America

Contents

Preface

THIS BOOK is written especially for those who are in high school. It will, however, be found equally interesting and helpful to parents, youth workers and all who are concerned with the problems facing young people. One of these problems concerns origins.

The vocabulary of this book has been kept nontechnical and within the scope required of tenth grade biology students. This fact makes it more readable for young people and for those who have not recently taken any formal science courses.

The author is a creationist who accepts the Bible as the Word of God and believes that He is the source of all things. This book is written within this framework. However, realizing that the average high school text takes organic evolution for granted, evidence is examined both for and against this theory. The points considered are those found most frequently in high school texts. Twelve texts have been examined critically, and a partial résumé of the evolutionary contents of each is given in a chart at the end of the book.

Except for a few, the chapters in this book have been divided into two parts, Evolutionary Interpretation and Creationist Interpretation. The points most commonly used in high school texts as evidence to support the theory of evolution are considered under the first heading. The fact that they are quoted does not mean that the author necessarily agrees with them. Under the second heading are given some of the weaknesses of the evolutionary position. It is shown that evolution is not the only unifying principle of biology, for creation by God is not only scientifically but biblically sound.

It would be a misconception to think that evolution is not still a much debated subject. For this reason the student is challenged to study God's Word and His created world and he is shown places where problems still exist. He is told that he might be the one to solve some of these problems. He is shown that Christianity and science need not be assigned to different areas of his life as is so often done. Christianity is not just for Sunday and science for school days.

The fact is emphasized that the position of the creationist does not rule out change within the biblical "kind." The limits of the various "kind" were fixed by the Creator. In some cases we do not know what these are, but we are studying to try to determine their limits.

I want to express my sincere thanks to many who have helped with the preparation of this book. Several men have reviewed part or all of my manuscript. The following have made helpful suggestions: Dr. Raymond Brand, Wheaton College, Ill.; Dr. James O. Buswell III, St. John's University, New York; Dr. George Howe, Los Angeles Baptist College; Dr. Russell Mixter, Wheaton College, Ill.; Dr. Wayne Frair, The King's College; and Dr. Martin Reno, Heidelberg College. These men hold a vital belief in the deity of Christ the Saviour and in the inspiration of God's Word. However, the criticisms and suggestions of those who interpret the Bible or science in a different way are as valuable as those whose views are the same on every subject. It is hoped that this book is strengthened by the fact that some of the men mentioned above hold different interpretations from those of the author.

For secretarial and editorial help I am grateful to Ruth Crow, Betty Daughenbaugh, Twila Haglin, Elsiebeth Mc-Daniel and Evelyn Reno.

Quotations from the Holy Bible are from the King James, or Authorized, Version unless otherwise noted.

Finally I would like to express my thanks to various book companies who have graciously allowed me to use material from their publications.

It is my prayer that this book will be helpful and be used for God's glory.

1

Your Bible and Science

HAVE YOU EVER STOPPED to think seriously about the relationship between the Bible and science? Science is an ever growing field, for today you can make a long list of things that are a common part of your way of life which were almost unknown a decade or so ago.

God has chosen to reveal Himself in three ways: in His written Word, the Bible; in His living Word, the Lord Jesus Christ; and in His created world, the universe. Perhaps you have never thought about God being revealed in the things you see around you and in the things you study in science. Some of the revelations about God observed in nature are presented in the Bible. "For ever since the creation of the world, His invisible characteristics—His eternal power and divine nature—have been made intelligible and clearly visible by His works" (Rom. 1:20, Williams). "The heavens declare the *glory* of God, and the firmament shows and proclaims His handiwork" (Ps. 19:1, Amplified). Even man was created for the glory of God (see Isa. 43:7).

As you study the structure of the atom or a complex part of the human body, or look at a beautiful sunset, you may say to yourself, These things show me some of the glory, power and handiwork of God. You might also agree that there are many things that we cannot learn about God by studying these created things around us. To learn the complete teaching concerning the great doctrines of the Christian faith, we must turn to the Scriptures to find the way to become new creations in Christ through faith in Him. This

9

faith does not come as a result of seeing God in His created world. However, after an individual becomes a Christian, the things of nature are more meaningful to him. Since both the written Word and the created things around us originated in a God of truth, they must agree. The study of them can never lead to a contradiction.

In making this last statement, we should not be blind to the realization that in our effort to find facts and how they should be interpreted we may follow three possible paths. Some people study only science, others study only the Bible, but some study both. Combining these studies is the best method. God has told us to study the things He has created. In Genesis 1:28 God says that man is to subdue the earth and have dominion over every living thing upon it. In our generation, more than in any other since this was spoken to Adam, men are learning about, conquering and bringing into subjection the things that God has made. Might not this command in Genesis include such things as studying and utilizing the power of electricity and the atom, improving our crops and domestic animals, and developing more beautiful and useful herbs and flowering plants?

Do not be afraid to investigate the facts of science. Some people hesitate to study them fearing they may find a contradiction between them and the Bible. Since both originate in God and since He is the Author of truth, no contradiction is possible. Why does there often seem to be a discrepancy between the two? The reason is that the men who gather and interpret the facts are imperfect and therefore their interpretations are imperfect at times. When we think there is a seeming conflict between science and the Bible we should reexamine both of them. By saying you should reexamine your interpretation of the Bible, we do not mean that we question in any way the truth of the Bible. We maintain a firm conviction that it is the inspired Word of God, the unerring and final guide to faith and life. In II Peter 1:21

we are told that men of old wrote the original manuscripts as they were moved to do so by God the Holy Spirit. However, there is a difference between inspiration and interpretation. About the first we say, "For ever, O Lord, Your Word [stands firm as the heavens] is settled in Heaven" (Ps. 119:89, Amplified). About the latter there can be a great variation.

As we study the subjects and various items contained in the different fields of science we do so with a realization that the Bible is different from all other books. As is mentioned in chapter 19, there are many reasons for making us realize that the Bible is the inspired Word of God. It has the power to change lives, it is indestructible, its prophecies and record of the Jewish people are accurate, as are other fulfilled prophecies. Its sixty-six books show a marvelous unity even though written by many different human instruments. Its authority is basic to our thinking.

Because this is true, do not be afraid to investigate anything the Bible contains. Some people hesitate to study the Bible along with science, fearing that they may find a contradiction between the two. This they will not find.

At times down through the years there has been a shift in thinking about what a particular scripture teaches. This has happened not because there was any change in God's established truth, but rather a change in man's imperfect interpretation of that truth. If you can understand this difference, you will have cleared a big hurdle in your thinking. Many people feel that a Christian should have little to do with science and should not seriously consider the discoveries in our present scientific explosion. But we are not making concessions to science when we thoughtfully study these new ideas because problems are not solved simply by closing our eyes to them. The problems involved in present-day science must be faced.

When we say that man has sometimes made imperfect interpretations of Scripture, we are not referring to subjects

that we consider the great fundamental doctrines of the
Christian faith. A person is not free to change his mind about
such essential, clearly presented doctrines as the incarnation,
death, burial and resurrection of Christ. If our thinking about
such fundamental truths is not firmly established, there is
danger that we will be "carried about with every wind of
doctrine" (Eph. 4:14). If you are not a Christian, will you
consider seriously these great truths, especially as given in
chapter 19. If you are a Christian, your feet are planted on
the Rock, the Lord Jesus Christ. However, you should realize that there is always more to learn. This is the reason
preachers continue to preach sermons, more books continue
to be printed about the Bible than about any other one subject, Bible colleges exist and Christians should always be
studying. With any new idea about either the Word or the
world, we should be neither gullible nor ignorant.

> Study and be eager and do your utmost to present
> yourself to God approved . . . a workman who has no
> cause to be ashamed, correctly analyzing and accurately
> dividing . . . the Word of Truth (II Tim. 2:15, Ampli-
> fied).

2

This Problem of Evolution

THE ORIGIN OF THE UNIVERSE, of the earth and of life and the variations we find among living things are especially interesting subjects. As we start thinking about them, the warning given in chapter 1 is very pertinent. Remember that since God is a God of truth and cannot lie, we need not hesitate to study His revelations, for each will complement the other. In them we will find neither contradiction nor error because they are ultimate truth if correctly interpreted. However, either the Bible or science can be imperfectly understood, interpreted and even perverted. Therefore each area must be studied thoughtfully and carefully.

If you are a Christian young person, you may find your science classroom a bewildering place. In a godly home, church and Sunday school you learned about creation as set forth in the Bible. Some of the beautiful things connected with creation are well expressed in Colossians:

> And Christ Himself is the Creator Who made everything in heaven and earth, the things we can see and the things we can't; the spirit world with its kings and kingdoms, its rulers and authorities: all were made by Christ for His own use and glory. He was before all else began and it is His power that holds everything together (Col. 1:16-17, Living Letters).

If you believe this, you find that as soon as you open the textbooks in schools, at either the elementary or high school level, you are faced with the theory of evolution. This makes your

classroom a challenging place because it leaves you not knowing what to believe. Your school teachers are educated men
and women whose word you should be able to accept as
truth; yet what they teach and believe sometimes contradicts
the Word of God. The authors of your textbooks are authorities in their fields, yet their presentation is presumably
based on the theory of evolution. This makes it hard to sort
out that which is fact from theory. This book is designed to
help you find the right path through this labyrinth in which
you may have been wandering.

The theory of evolution is not an established fact. The
evidence in nature may be differently interpreted. The
side teaching organic evolution is the only one usually presented in elementary and high school books and, since these
pupils are not able to evaluate the theory, it is usually accepted without question. In advanced books the limitations
of the various statements given in its favor are much more
freely admitted. There is this "other side" of the theory.

The points most commonly used in high school texts to
support the theory are considered in this book. These differ
somewhat from those found in college texts. The evidence
offered to support the theory of evolution is given largely in
the form of quotations from the most widely used high school
books. Following each presentation there is a short discussion. In some cases the statements have very little to do with
the theory; or else the truth that is in it is given a twist to
make it conform to the evolutionist's preconceived belief.

Before presenting the statements used to substantiate the
theory, let us clarify the meaning of the word "evolution."
The word itself simply means "change." If nothing more
were included, we would have to say that we all are evolutionists! All around us in both living and nonliving things we
see continual change. However, much more than this is implied in the way in which we and our texts will be using the
word. The theory began many years before Christ, but its

greatest impetus was due to the work of Charles Darwin a little over a century ago. The evolutionist says that, by change, *all* living forms in the world today have been produced from one or a few common ancestors. There has been change in the past, but convincing evidence does not support the theory that this much change has taken place.

Many evolutionists use the term "macroevolution" to designate change between the higher categories and the term "microevolution" for that between lower ones as the genera and species. We do not use the latter term because practically all high school books use the word "evolution" to refer only to the former concept. We could use the word "evolution" to mean diversification from the created "kind," or change within a certain group, but we do not. "Evolution" as used in this book refers to "the succession of changes by which organisms pass from a simple to a complex condition." As some high school texts use the term "amoeba-to-man evolution," we do the same.

As we proceed in this book we call attention to the amount of change that can be produced by either artificial or natural means. In a certain sense this change might be called "evolution" but we do not so use the word. As we use it here, we mean change from one group to another so that all living things in the world (both plants and animals) are related one to the other.

This is the way some of the writers of biology texts state it:

> Through a long series of changes, so slight as to be unnoticeable in even thousands of years, man was formed. All plants and animals have a similar history. The beginnings of plants and animals go back to the origin of life itself, and over the course of time their descendants have changed to become the animals and plants of today. This is EVOLUTION, once hotly debated, but now a well-established theory.[1]

[1]Biological Science Curriculum Study, *Biological Science: An Inquiry into Life*, Yellow Version, p. 7.

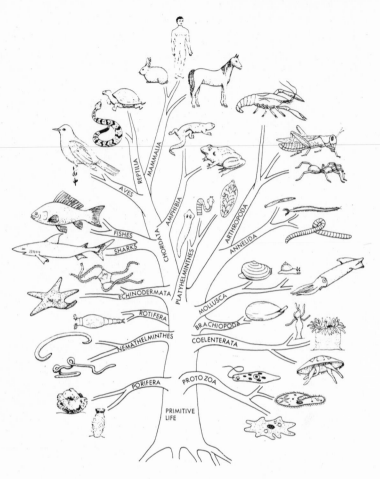

Figure 1

Phyla of the animal kingdom arranged like the limbs of a tree. This picture is typical of the concept most high school books present concerning the theory of evolution. It is found in *Biology For You* by B. B. Vance and D. F. Miller (used by permission of J. B. Lippincott & Co.). They say that the animal phyla can be arranged like the limbs of a tree. The limbs closest together are thought to be most closely related.

Another book states it this way:

> The complex forms, then, are descended from simpler forms; and all are related, some more, and some less closely. That is what is meant by the evolution of living things, or organic evolution.[2]

When an organic evolutionist states that he thinks that all living things are related, he also includes man, as is shown here:

> [Darwin's] ideas ran counter to the science and religion of his day. The principle criticism came from those who believed that he reduced man's position from the center of all living things to that of a single species, subject to the same evolutionary processes as other species.[3]

Figure 1 is typical of the way most high school books present the evolutionary idea concerning the supposed development of animals.

A few books present the "bush" pattern of evolution. The uppermost tips of the branches represent currently living forms, and branches terminating below the top represent extinct forms. The trunk pictures the ancestor of all living things.

These quotations are from a book that in its context makes it clear that the author believes all living things are related:

> The evidence that evolution has occurred is so overwhelming that no one who is acquainted with it has any doubt that new species are derived from previous ones by descent with modification. [They] . . . provide overwhelming proof that organic evolution has occurred.[4]

These four quotations are sufficient to show how evolution traces all plant and animal life back to a single-cell ancestor. In this sense the word "evolution" is used, since that is how it is used in the textbooks being examined. Nearly all take

[2]E. Kroeber, W. H. Wolff, and R. I. Weaver, *Biology*, p. 485.
[3]W. H. Gregory and E. H. Goldman, *Biological Science*, p. 732.
[4]C. A. Villee, *Biology*, pp. 592-610.

it for granted that everyone believes it and that it is the only possible explanation for things seen in the world around us. As one text says, "All reputable biologists have agreed that the evolution of life on the earth is an established fact."[5] And as stated above, the BSCS committee says evolution was "once hotly debated, but [is] now a well-established theory."[6]

Remember that it is a theory. A theory has value *if* it makes you study and examine more than one side of a question. As you continue to read this book, we hope that you will do this, for many have accepted the theory without doing any critical thinking. They may have accepted it because they found it so widely taught; or, they may have been influenced to believe it because it was so ingeniously presented or, perhaps because some very learned people sincerely believe it. Some may be influenced toward evolution because they see around them human inventions, activities and organizations that start with the small and simple and then increase in complexity. These criteria are not satisfactory means of judging the validity of a theory, so read the following chapters carefully and think about the Scripture references used. We hope this exposition will help direct you to a better understanding of this controversial subject.

[5]B. B. Vance and D. F. Miller, *Biology for You*, p. 531.
[6]BSCS, Yellow Version, *ibid.*

3

Similarity and Relationship

EVOLUTIONARY INTERPRETATION

ONE OF THE CHIEF STATEMENTS used to support the theory of evolution is that similarity among living things shows their relationship one to the other. Therefore this idea is considered first. This concept, that kinship is shown by similarities, is basic to the theory. It is a premise that overlaps many of the others and for the sake of emphasis is referred to a number of times. Much of the similarity argument used here may be applied to such topics as embryology, comparative anatomy, physiological activity and biochemistry. Although this quotation is primarily concerned with anatomy, the argument could not be stated more clearly than it is in Gregory's text:

> In studying the skeletons of widely different vertebrates, the comparative anatomist finds basic similarities of structure. For example, consider the forelimbs of man, whale, bat and horse. In man, the forelimbs are hands adapted for manipulation. In the whale, they are flippers adapted for swimming. In the bat the forelimbs are wings. In the horse the forelimbs are legs adapted for running. In each case five fingers, or *phalanges*, may be found. In the whale, the phalanges are imbedded in the flipper. In the bat, the phalanges are elongated into the wing supports. In the horse, they are gathered into bone splints above the hoof.
>
> The limbs of men, whales, bats and horses are used for different purposes but have the same plan of construc-

tion. To the biologist, this similarity of structure indicates common descent. He refers to organs having the same structural plan as **homologus organs.** Homologus organs are believed to originate from some common ancestor in the remote past. As descendants develop along different lines, a change in usage gradually results.[1]

This idea, that similarity shows a common ancestry in the remote past, is shown in the sketches of Figure 2.

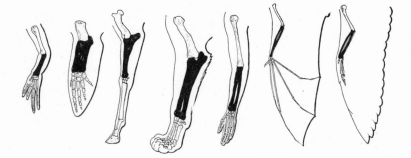

Figure 2

Homologous bones in the forelimbs of seven vertebrates—from left to right, the foreleg of a frog, the flipper of a whale, the foreleg of a horse and of a lion, the arm of man, and the wing of a bat and of a bird. (Used by permission of Biological Science Curriculum Study.)

In most high school texts, this concept about homologous structures is pushed back to the point of saying that all living things are related. The evolutionist assumes that all living things come from one simple form of life and therefore it is to be expected that likenesses will exist. As previously mentioned, advanced books do not always present this picture.

[1]W. H. Gregory and E. H. Goldman, *Biological Science*, pp. 707-8.

CREATIONIST INTERPRETATION

In considering this subject, first of all it is true that similarities often show relationship. We must face this truth honestly before pointing out some of its weaknesses and limitations. We all recognize that there are similarities of different degrees among plants and among animals, and some of these similarities show different degrees of relationship.

It is easy to see what we mean by this when we consider the likenesses we see in different men. Caucasian men look more like each other than they look like Negroes. Within the Caucasian race, Scandinavians look more like each other than they look like Italians. Within the Italian nationality, members of the same family often show a family resemblance. Identical twins within that family will look even more alike because there is a closer relationship. In this example we see that the more closely related men are by race, nationality, family or twinning, the greater is the similarity.

Therefore, this is not just an evolutionary argument; it usually is quite obvious. The same is also true of other groups. Just as from an originally created pair, such as Adam and Eve, can come offspring that differ greatly, so from an originally created pair of ancestors of horses or dogs or chickens can come a great variety of horses and dogs and chickens. They show certain similarities because they exhibit various degrees of relationship, as indicated in Figure 3.

Another thought that comes to the mind of a Christian to explain likenesses between living things is that they could be the result of a common plan in the mind of God the Creator. In fact, that would be the logical thing to expect because there is no reason why God should not have used a similar general plan for many animals. When living things have the same physical functions, it would be natural that the equipment for these functions would be similar. God logically would give the same structure to animals who were to walk the same earth, breathe the same air and eat the same food. The great Designer might have used another general plan for animals that were to fly in the air and another for those that were to live in the water.

God is omnipotent. He could have used a different plan for each living creature; He could have created all kinds of

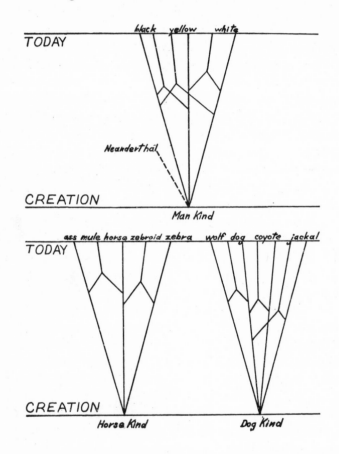

Figure 3

Chart showing the relationship between a possible created "kind" and forms living today (from Wayne Frair and P. William Davis, *The Case for Creation*).

weird animals with different combinations of numbers of legs, ears, eyes and heads. It is not a question of what He is able to do, but what He actually did. As creationists, we believe that God created groups of plants and animals according to a general plan and gave them certain similarities at the time they were created.

Likenesses that are attributed to God as Designer may also be the result of kinship, one thing for the other. For instance, a collie and a shepherd dog may look something alike. This can be both because God designed each of them and also because they are related. These two ideas, giving causes for the similarities seen in plants and animals, are not mutually exclusive. Both can be true at the same time.

One of the difficulties in trying to give credence to the theory of evolution by saying that similarities show relationship is seen in the fact that it cannot be carried out consistently. Certain parts of some animals show likenesses to the same parts of other animals, whereas other parts of these same animals show dissimilarities. The evolutionist will say that it is a matter of weighing the various characteristics and picking out those that are most important to show the specific relationship he is trying to present.

You should be aware of this situation and some examples will help. The similarity in skeleton of the Tasmanian wolf and the dog is used by the evolutionist as evidence of their close relationship. However, the Tasmanian wolf is a marsupial, carrying its young in a pouch, whereas the dog is not a marsupial. This latter fact would indicate that the two are not closely related.

Another example is found in the African scorpion and the lobster, each of which has a large pinching claw. According to the evolutionist this resemblance should show close relationship and yet in this case he says that they are distantly related because the claws are on different appendages.

The Australian platypus has a bill and webbed feet which

resemble a duck. However, it is classed as a mammal because it has milk glands with which to feed its young. In
this and other ways it is very unlike a bird. One cannot say
that a platypus has close kinship to the birds because they
both have bills, and at the same time to the mammals because of the presence of milk glands.

Another difficulty is a type of similarity that all scientists
agree does not result from common inheritance; it is often
known as parallel mutations. In a zoo on the same day might
be born a deer and a bear, both of which are albinos. Because there was some change in the germ cells of these animals, they look very different from their parents and are
called mutations. However, no one would suggest that these
albino deer and bear are closely related because they both
lack pigment. The likeness just happened to appear simul-
taneously in the two animals.

In one text with the use of colored pictures of birds is shown
another reason why likeness in appearance is not a reliable
guide to kinship.[2] Male and female red-winged blackbirds
are pictured to show that even though these birds belong to
the same species, the sexes appear to be very dissimilar. The
adult male and the immature male indigo bunting look so
dissimilar that one would never think they belonged to the
same species. The Arcadian flycatcher and the Least flycatcher are pictured with the comment that the two birds
look so much alike that it is hard to tell them apart, but the
bird populations they represent do not interbreed. The likeness is only superficial.

In summary, similarities can be used to point to creation
by God, the great Designer, or to the fact that the plants or
animals really have had a common ancestor. Although sometimes there is truth in the fact that unrelated animals may
appear to be similar, this is not good evidence for evolution.

[2]Biological Science Curriculum Study, *High School Biology: BSCS Green
Version*, pp. 46-47.

It is not a consistent argument because certain parts of some animals are similar whereas other parts of the same animals are very unlike. Internal parts may show one thing and external parts another. Some similarities are the result of parallel mutations and not of kinship. Similarity is often superficial: some animals that look alike are not able to interbreed. Animals of the same species which would be expected to look similar may differ greatly because of sex or age.

At the beginning of this chapter we said that this argument was basic to the theory of organic evolution. More than any other single concept, it is the foundation upon which many of the parts of the theory are based. If the foundation is shaky, the building is likely to be weak. This is true of the theory of evolution—it is built on the shaky foundation that "similarity indicates kinship."

4

The Testimony of Geology and Paleontology

Two of the most crucial subjects connected with the study of evolution are geology and paleontology. The latter word means the science that "deals with the finding, cataloguing, and interpretation of the abundant and diverse evidence of life in former times."[1] If evidence for the theory is to be found anywhere, it will be in the rocks and fossils. Therefore they warrant careful study. The rock strata and the fossils in them are objective evidence and the information about them is much the same in all books. Fossils can accurately tell us what living things were like even though they lived thousands of years ago.

Fossils are plants or animals, or their parts or imprints, petrified or preserved in rocks or other substances like ice, tar or amber. By far the most common fossils are the ones found in sedimentary rocks. These were formed under water as material settled to the bottom and covered plants and animals that had died. Later there had to be drying up of this water, a lifting of the land, and still later an erosion to expose the fossils.

Since the beginning of creation, there seem to have been long periods of time when water covered land areas and then retreated. There have been earthquakes, glaciers and floods. Rocks have been depressed, elevated, folded and even slid one on top of another, which has resulted in their being found

[1]C. A. Villee, *Biology*, p. 692.

in all sorts of positions. Sometimes the older ones are even found on top of the younger ones. The study of geology, therefore, is by no means easy, but the rocks and their fossils have a valuable story to tell us. It is a story that we should study carefully if we hope to learn more about the way God has worked in our world in the past. Do not be afraid to study this story even though some of the facts may be new.

The study of fossils might be likened to that of space exploration. In both fields, the facts and figures of last year, or even of last month, often need revision. As we continue to develop new dating methods and learn more about the rocks and fossils, we must update our theories about plants and animals that lived in the past and about events that took place then.

Do not misunderstand and think that we mean that the truth of the Bible ever changes. It is our one sure foundation. However, the Bible gives little or no information about many of the subjects in science. In these areas we are free to set up our theories and study these things, being careful as we do so to stay within the framework of the Word of God.

The conclusions reached by the evolutionist and by the nonevolutionist are different largely because they approach this field with previously formed different philosophies. If a person is working within a framework that excludes miracles, his conclusions will naturally be different from those of a person who takes these for granted.

EVOLUTIONARY INTERPRETATION

The fact that data from the fields of geology and paleontology is used to support the theory of evolution can be seen in these quotations:

> One of the main lines of investigation which reveals the time course of past evolution is paleontology, the study of fossils.[2]

[2]P. B. Weisz, *The Science of Biology*, p. 719.

MAJOR STRATIGRAPHIC AND TIME DIVISIONS IN USE BY THE U.S. GEOLOGICAL SURVEY

Era or Eratem	System or Period		Series or Epoch	Estimated ages of time boundaries in millions of years
Cenozoic	Quaternary		Holocene	
			Pleistocene	2-3[1]
	Tertiary		Pliocene	12[1]
			Miocene	26[2]
			Oligocene	37-38
			Eocene	53-54
			Paleocene	65
Mesozoic	Cretaceous[4]		Upper (Late)	
			Lower (Early)	136
	Jurassic		Upper (Late)	
			Middle (Middle)	
			Lower (Early)	190-195
	Triassic		Upper (Late)	
			Middle (Middle)	
			Lower (Early)	225
Paleozoic	Permian[4]		Upper (Late)	
			Lower (Early)	280
	Carboniferous Systems	Pennsylvanian[4]	Upper (Late)	
			Middle (Middle)	
			Lower (Early)	
		Mississippian[4]	Upper (Late)	
			Lower (Early)	345
	Devonian		Upper (Late)	
			Middle (Middle)	
			Lower (Early)	395
	Silurian[4]		Upper (Late)	
			Middle (Middle)	
			Lower (Early)	430-440
	Ordovician[4]		Upper (Late)	
			Middle (Middle)	
			Lower (Early)	500
	Cambrian[4]		Upper (Late)	
			Middle (Middle)	
			Lower (Early)	570
	Precambrian[4]		Informal subdivisions such as upper, middle, and lower, or upper and lower, or younger and older may be used locally.	3,600+[3]

[1] Holmes, Arthur, 1964, Principles of physical geology: 2d ed., New York, Ronald Press, p. 360-361, for the Pleistocene and Pliocene; and Obradovich, J. D., 1965, Age of marine Pleistocene of California: Am. Assoc. Petroleum Geologists, v. 49, no. 7, p. 1087, for the Pleistocene of southern California.

[2] Geological Society of London, 1964, The Phanerozoic time-scale; a symposium: Geol. Soc. London, Quart. Jour., v. 120, supp., p. 260-262, for the Miocene through the Cambrian.

[3] Stern, T. W., written commun., 1968, for the Precambrian.

[4] Includes provincial series accepted for use in U.S. Geological Survey reports.

Terms designating time are in parentheses. Informal time terms early, middle, and late may be used for the eras, and for periods where there is no formal subdivision into Early, Middle, and Late, and for epochs. Informal rock terms lower, middle, and upper may be used where there is no formal subdivision of a system or of a series.

GEOLOGIC NAMES COMMITTEE, 1968

Figure 4

Geological Time Chart

The extensive fossil record provides evidence of organic evolution and gives the details of the evolutionary relationship of many lines of descent.[3]

Fossils are embedded in successive layers and so provide a time picture of evolution.[4]

Though we may never be able to trace the evolution of all living forms through the fossils of their ancestors, the presence and distribution of their fossils already discovered provide us with some of the most direct evidence of the theory of evolution.[5]

Over a long period of time, rocks have gradually been laid down to form a stratigraphic column with the oldest at the bottom. For convenience, geological time has been divided into various subdivisions. Most high school texts give a table similar to Figure 4 (published by the U.S. Geological Survey).

Note the location of Figure 4 for the names on it are referred to in various chapters of this book. This view of geological history is called a uniformitarian position which means that the various rock strata over the past millions of years have been laid down at a nearly uniform rate, approximately in the same manner in which they are being laid down today. At no one place on earth is a complete stratigraphic column found. Parts from one place in the world are filled in with parts from another place to try to close the gaps and make a complete column. Using this stratigraphic column, the evolutionist states that the deeper one probes into the layers of rock, the simpler are the fossils that are found. To him, this is a picture of the more simple plants and animals developing first and all present forms evolving from them.

[3]Villee, p. 592.
[4]*Ibid.*, p. 720.
[5]J. W. Kimball, *Biology*, p. 543.

CREATIONIST INTERPRETATION

Earlier in this chapter it was noted that rocks and fossils are two of the most important subjects for any scientist to examine. They are a record of past events for which the evolutionist and the nonevolutionist alike are trying to find a correct explanation. The facts are in the rock strata and in the fossils, but the explanation and interpretation of those facts necessarily involve theories.

Because theories are involved in the areas of geology and paleontology, there is a difference of opinion. At the present time the majority of Christian scientists accept most of the information given in the geological time chart. The majority of Christian scientists are uniformitarians in that they hold this position as concerns the formation of the rocks and fossils, but *not* that the fossils show all life having originated from a single cell. There does not need to be a connection between accepting the material given in the geological time chart and accepting evolution. Further study will show that the two do not need to be connected.

Although the majority of Christian scientists hold the uniformitarian position, many have serious doubts that this is an adequate answer to many geological and paleontological questions. In chapter 15 it is shown that there is quite a variety of theories held by Christians. (In that chapter it is stated that this is not a closed field, but the reader is challenged to further study.) It is possible that no one has found the right answer yet. It is certain that we have not yet found a theory that answers *all* of the questions in these fields. The uniformitarian view is presented because the author feels it comes closest to harmonizing the facts.

Therefore, let us continue thinking about the type of work involved in setting up a stratigraphic column. Scientists know the average rate of the laying down of the different types of sediment that go to make up the rocks. This and other information is used to calculate the age of a particular rock. It is realized that from time to time the factors that control these rates of rock formation may undergo changes. However, no evidence indicates that the rate was ever very different from the present one. Thus, the approximate dates given for the various eras and other time periods represent reasonable deductions based on average rates of deposition. Geological time has been divided into various subdivisions in much the same way as historical time has been divided into segments on the basis of what men did at a particular time. We speak of such historical periods as the Dark Ages and the Renaissance. These periods are part of the Christian era. In much the same way, geologists divide the earth's history into great eras. Some of these eras are divided into periods, and then subdivided into epochs.

In the high school books being used, considerable variation exists in the number of years given for these time divisions. This is especially true when dealing with the older eras. Dates are not being thrown around loosely when it is said that one cannot be sure of the time of an event to within a few million years. It is just being realistic to admit that old dates are likely to be less definite. For example, it is much easier to place in the right decade the presidency of Abraham Lincoln than to give the correct decade for the reign of Nero. Even this is easier than to think back and correctly place the reign of one of the Egyptian pharaohs. By extending this idea and going back into prehistoric times, the farther back one goes, the harder it becomes to determine preciseness. An accurate date is also likely to be less important in the early part of the earth's history.

For a long time people have thought that the earth is very, very old. Before the discovery of radioactive methods of dating, any estimate of the age of the earth was based on many variables. These older methods of dating did, and still do, have some value, especially for comparatively recent ages. Because it is important to know something about dating methods, a number will be mentioned, but limited space allows little evaluation of them.

Very roughly, dating methods fall into two categories. First, there are those that give information about the latest few hundred or thousand years. Because the dates obtained in this way can often be validated by comparison with historical dates, they can be used to fill in gaps where history leaves us no record. Second, there are the newer methods that involve measurement of amounts of radioactive elements and are especially useful in establishing dates that run into the millions and billions of years. In addition to the dating methods that are a help in determining the age of the earth, there are also those that can be used to help in dating the stars and other bodies in our universe. In the book *Science Speaks*[6] are discussions of the age of meteorites, tides between the earth and moon, age determination of the sun, star streaming and our expanding universe.

Consider some of these dating methods. Some of the simple ones are probably familiar, for example, the growth rings of a tree. By examining cross sections of giant redwoods that have been cut down, or by borings taken out of live trees, it is possible to tell such things as the date of a drought that existed a couple of thousands of years ago. The General Sherman tree still standing in Sequoia National Park is estimated to be thirty-five hundred years old. Especially in the Southwest are found petrified trees which have had their wood slowly replaced by mineral deposits.

Studying tree rings provides information about the last few thousand years, but studying those of petrified wood takes one back to more ancient life. Many things can be told about these areas which were once covered with forests, later by water while the wood was becoming petrified, and which are now largely deserts.

For dating material that is only a few thousand years old,

[6]Peter W. Stoner, *Science Speaks*.

one method uses pollen grains. Different plants produce characteristic pollen. Grains which fell many years ago were sometimes preserved in peat moss and bogs. It is possible, by studying pollen grains found at different depths, to know something about such things as when pine trees grew in a particular area and when the tree growth changed to some other kind.

Knowing what kinds of plant lived in a certain place is a clue as to what kinds of animal could have lived there. Pollen from domesticated plants tells one when farmers might have settled in the area. By this method one learns that the Palace of Fine Arts in Mexico City is built on what used to be the site of an ancient lake. Before laying the foundation for this building, drilling machines brought up cores of rock and soil containing eighty-thousand-year-old pollen from wild grass that may have been an ancestor of our modern corn.

No absolute dates can be found by this method, but the comparative information helps to give a picture of what life used to be like in certain prehistoric times.

The amount of fluorine in fossils helps in assigning a certain age to them. The longer bones stay in the ground, the more fluorine they absorb from the soil. Again, this does not give us absolute dates because the soil at different places on the earth's surface contains different amounts of fluorine. Nevertheless, by this method it can be told which bones are older and which more recent, if they have been found in the same body of earth.

One dating method is based on calculating the rate of sedimentation and the rate at which rock was formed in the past and is still being formed.

Another method involves the rate at which erosion wears away land areas. Rock formations are studied and measurements made of the amount of time required to remove a small portion. This is then multiplied by the total amount already

removed and thus an estimate is made of the length of time
since the erosion began to take place. This is being done in
connection with the rate at which (1) the rocks under Nia-
gara Falls are being worn back, (2) the Grand Canyon of
Colorado is being cut, and (3) the Appalachian Mountains
are being worn down.

Another method that has been used in the past for determining geological age concerns the rate at which the oceans
are increasing in salt concentration. Although it is little used
today, most high school texts still carry an account of this
method, but usually with some qualifying phrase such as "it
has some value."

It is not an unfounded assumption that at the time of creation the oceans may have been composed of fresh water. As
a hot earth cooled, water vapor (free from minerals) con-
densed and fell on its surface. Some of this water formed the
oceans and some fell on the land areas. By way of the rivers
and streams, some of the rain ran into the oceans, taking with
it the salt and other minerals that were leached out of the
soil over which the water flowed. As the water evaporated,
it left behind the salt, thus increasing the total amount that
the oceans contained.

This increase in concentration is still taking place now. In
keeping with changing conditions, this rate of increase may
have varied from age to age, and it cannot be used to arrive
at any absolute date for the formation of a cool earth. However, it does help one to realize that the earth is very old.
In some parts of the world there are caves containing huge
stalactites and stalagmites. Those of the Mammoth Cave or
Carlsbad Caverns show that a long period of time was involved in their formation.

Coral islands gradually built up from the secretions of tiny
animals also help one to realize that the earth is very old.
The March, 1967, *Reader's Digest* in an article entitled "Australia's Great Barrier Reef" says:

It is hard to believe that the architects of this vast realm of guile and beauty are creatures hardly bigger than a pinhead, unable to see, hear or even move about. Yet over the eons, these insignificant organisms have built up the Great Barrier, inch by inch, mile by square mile. . . . As successive generations of coral colonies die, their innumerable trillions of skeletons gradually pile higher and higher.[7]

Gypsum layers hundreds of feet thick are found in the Southwest. At the present rate of deposition, it would take tens of thousands of years for these to form.

Specimen Ridge in Yellowstone National Park is a two-thousand-foot cliff. A cross section of it shows eighteen petrified forests arranged in linear fashion, one on top of the other. It would have taken an immense amount of time for each forest to grow to maturity, be destroyed by volcanic ash and then have a succeeding forest grow on top of it.

These things just mentioned (salt concentration, sedimentation, erosion, stalactites and stalagmites, formation of coral islands, gypsum formation, petrified forests and others) lead us to infer that the earth is millions of years old. By considering them we are *forced* to this conclusion. The dates arrived at by these methods cannot be precise and are generally used in connection with the relative length of time of certain parts of the earth's history rather than in determining the earth's total age.

Granted, these ways of determining age are rather crude because everyone acknowledges that at different times the forces of nature may vary greatly. For example, such things as rain, wind and temperature could speed up or slow down erosion. The rate at which erosion is now taking place may not be exactly the same as in the past but surely it is some indication of what it was like in former times.

Much of today's research makes use of dating methods

[7]Francis and Katharine Drake, "Australia's Great Barrier Reef," *Reader's Digest*. Vol. XC, No. 539 (March, 1967), p. 162.

that have been discovered in recent years. The very fact that they are quite new causes some people to be skeptical about using them, whereas the same person may readily accept scientific advances in other fields. As cautioned elsewhere, do not jump to conclusions but, at the same time, do not hesitate to make use of information that is as well authenticated as are some of the newer dating methods. Carbon 14 is one of these newer means of determining dates. Since its discovery, some of the information about artifacts, rocks and fossils has had to be changed. In some cases using this method has substantiated early estimates, and in other cases revisions have had to be made.

When one reads that the date of some event has been changed, one should not make fun of the scientist but rather realize that this is what he expects in his field of study. In no field, be it botany or zoology, chemistry or physics, geology or astronomy, has a person ever been able to walk in and find the problems all solved and the information ready for him to put to use.

Extensive work with the carbon 14 method began in the late 1940's; since then it has been improved and widely used even though it is still being refined. Cosmic rays in the upper atmosphere act on nitrogen to produce radioactive carbon 14 which, as well as the more common carbon 12, combines with the oxygen in the air to produce carbon dioxide. During the process of photosynthesis, carbon 14 is incorporated into the plants. At the time of their death, plants and animals contain a known amount of carbon 14 because it has reached an equilibrium with that in the air. After death, of course, no more enters the system and what is there starts to disintegrate. The amount of radiation given off is fairly constant and continuous and can be measured with a Geiger counter. The more clicks heard per given time unit, the more recent the death of the organism; the fewer the clicks, the longer the time.

Since the half-life of carbon 14 is known to be about 5,760 years, at the end of that time the amount of carbon 14 left in the plant or animal body will be half of what it was at the time of its death. At the end of another 5,760 years, that amount will again be cut in half. The half-life of carbon 14 is relatively short compared with some other units, therefore this method of age determination ceases to be useful as material approaches an age of about 40,000 years, or about seven half-lives of carbon 14.

When this method was first worked out, tests were made on substances of known age to establish its validity. For example, a funeral boat was tested from a tomb in Egypt. The known historical date and the carbon 14 date showed good agreement, in this case about a hundred years.

This method has been of incalculable help to scientists. Suppose a scientist were trying to learn something of the American Indian cliff dwellers of Arizona. Maybe he had spent years studying the location of the caves, the rock strata, the fossils and artifacts found in and around the caves. His study would have led him to the conclusion that Indians of a particular cave probably lived there about 12,000 years ago. Now suppose he had a wooden tool or weapon found in one of the dwellings he was studying. He could have a piece of this wood tested by the carbon 14 method. At the present time he could send it to a laboratory in New Jersey and have this test run for $150. If the test report showed the wood to have an age of about 12,000 years, it is obvious how helpful this would be in confirming other estimates.

One of the recently discovered ways of dating some materials is called "fission tracking." Bits of volcanic glass and also traces of Uranium 238 are found in many places in the world. This latter substance, being radioactive, divided at a regular rate, leaving "fission tracks" in the glass. Under the microscope, these resemble tiny grooves which can be counted and thus provide a measure of the time that has passed since that glass cooled.

This procedure is quite straightforward for large single crystals or for homogeneous glass which has a concentration of one or more parts per million by weight of uranium. Of course this greatly oversimplifies the picture and several things may cause an error in the date at which one arrives. It is fortunate that the possible sources of error in the fission-tracking method are different from the sources that might cause an error in one of the other methods, so one is used to check against the other.

Recently this fission-tracking method was employed at General Electric and led researchers to the conclusion that lava at the bottom of the Olduvai Gorge in Africa, where the fossil bones of Zinjanthropus were found, is around 1,750,000 years old. These fossils are mentioned again in chapter 14. Potassium-argon dating, when used on material in the same gorge, showed dates of 1,500,000 to 1,750,000 years of age.

The Potassium-argon dating method tests volcanic ash that contains a radioactive form of the element potassium. When it decays it forms calcium and argon. The half-life of this potassium 40 is 1,300 million years so this method can be used on things that are very old. When employing this method, a scientist uses an apparatus called a mass spectrometer to measure the amount of argon 40 in a certain rock. Since he knows the rate at which the argon is formed, he can tell the date at which the first argon was produced, which is likely the date of the rock's formation.

Estimating the age of rocks by use of uranium 238 is another method. Uranium 238 disintegrates slowly, forming an isotope of lead which is recognizable because it is different from the regular lead with which we are more familiar. In four and one-half billion years, half of this element transforms itself into lead. If one should find in a pocket of undisturbed rock a certain amount of uranium 238 and a certain amount of lead, it would be possible to estimate how long it would have taken for this amount of lead to be produced. This gives a fairly accurate minimum age for that rock. By this method some rocks are shown to be many millions of years old.

Scientists agree that much work is yet to be done. The results, especially when working with these very old dates, are open to revision. However, the radioactive methods mentioned, as well as ones using thorium, strontium and rubidium, are proving very helpful. As mentioned, older dating methods such as those based on rates of sedimentation and erosion were open to serious fluctuations and error because the processes upon which they were based changed with changing conditions. The radioactive methods are not influenced by ordinary environmental changes of heat, magnetic and electrical fields, vacuum or light. With the discovery of these better methods, information about the old age of the earth has been substantiated or revisions have been made.

As noted previously, the majority of Christians accept as fairly accurate the dates given in the geological time chart at the beginning of this chapter. At the present time it offers the best explanation for an interpretation of geology and paleontology, even though it may need constant revision as knowledge increases. Accepting these dates should in no way be construed to mean that one is accepting the theory of evolution or even "giving ground to the evolutionist." And they certainly do not contradict any biblical facts.

In connection with dating the rocks and fossils, someone may condemn what is called "reasoning in a circle." It is said that the rocks are used to tell the age of the fossils and then that the fossils are used to tell the age of the rocks. This had to be done in the past as information about the age of both of these things was being accumulated. Since radioactive dating has now been refined enough to give a

fair degree of accuracy, this is no longer the case. As the
dates and sequence of the rocks in the stratigraphic column
have been confirmed by radioactive dating, so also has a
fairly good idea of the dates and sequence of the fossils been
formed. Not that any one dating method, radioactive or
otherwise, is infallible, but most scientists feel that there are
now enough methods so that one can be checked against
another. Many people are not willing to accept new discoveries in this field, whereas they readily do so in other
scientific areas. Largely because they fear it will be tending
toward an acceptance of some part of evolution, many people are afraid of such things as the use of dates that run into
the millions and billions of years. Do not be confused into
thinking that new scientific information in such fields as
geology and paleontology is necessarily antibiblical. The
Bible and science are friends and agree with each other.
They were produced by the same Designer and were given
for our study and edification.

In relation to our subject, the significance of all of this
discussion concerning the age of the earth and of the rocks
is simply this: rocks contain fossils, and fossils are the best
key as to whether evolution has or has not taken place. If
we know something about the age of the rocks, we will also
know something about the age of the fossils they contain.
Now let us turn our attention to the fossils.

If one looks at an eroded hillside several hundred feet high
and made up of many layers of sedimentary rock, he concludes at least two things: (1) it probably took a long time
for the formation of such a hill, and (2) those rocks near
the bottom of the hill must be older than the ones near the
surface.

A little observation, work and reasoning would show other
things. If one dug into the cliff near its base, in certain rocks
he would find fossils of plants and animals both similar to
the ones living today and ones which were different.

Even though one were far away from any body of water he might find some fossils of sea shells. He would reason that they had been carried in from some distance and deposited there, or that water had once covered that area for long enough time for them to have taken up that place as their normal habitat.

Some of the plants and animals whose fossils are found are now extinct. Evidence points to the fact that some of them became extinct millions of years ago and some of them in comparatively recent times. The dinosaurs evidently became extinct before man was created for they and man are not found in the same rock strata. Mammoths that may have lived ten thousand years ago, however, were hunted by man, and the spearpoints that killed them have been found with the fossil bones.

In many places of the earth are enormous numbers of fossils—sometimes millions and even billions in a small area. An example is the diatomaceous earth found in a large quarry in the Lompoc Valley of California. Diatoms are very small plants belonging to the algae which have an almost shell-like covering which varies in size and shape. Their beautiful patterns are revealed under the microscope. There can be no doubt that billions of them lived in this particular area at about the same time because their shells have been dug out of these quarries by the ton.

Many interesting fossils preserved in tar have been found in the Rancho La Brea pits in Los Angeles. Quantities of skeletons of the giant sloth, elephants, saber-toothed tigers and many kinds of insects taken from these pits can be seen in the Los Angeles County Museum of Arts and Science in Exposition Park in Los Angeles.

Examples of collections of numerous fossils can be given many times. Therefore it is readily recognized that certain forms of life were once much more abundant than they are now. Such abundant forms are often found chiefly in certain layers of rocks, and so are spoken of as being the dominant form at the time that rock was formed. Because of the differences in organisms found between layers of rocks, one knows that some plants and animals that were dominant at one time have changed through the ages.

The next subject concerns the location of the different fossils. Look back in this chapter at the geological time table and find the period of time marked Precambrian. This is often subdivided into the Archeozoic era, in the rocks of which have been found no living things, and the Proterozoic era, in which some think there are indications of simple forms of water life.

In regard to the Cambrian rocks, generally believed to be half a billion years old, several interesting things are noted. First, in these rocks is found a large quantity of fossils in great variety. Sometimes this is even spoken of as the "Cambrian explosion." With the exception of some of the vertebrates, most of the major groups are represented here. There are jelly fish, sponges, worms, snails and trilobites. Instead of finding that these evolved one from the other, they are found suddenly appearing in the rocks with their complex systems and organs fully formed and functioning. To the Christian the picture is one of creation. To one who leaves biblical, miraculous creation out of his thinking, there is no satisfactory answer for the quantity, variety and complexity of the Cambrian fossils. Weisz seems to be completely evolutionary in his position but he says:

> It is a very curious circumstance that rocks older than about 500 million years are so barren of fossils, whereas rocks younger than that are comparatively rich in them. Many hypotheses have been proposed to account for this, but to date a satisfactory explanation has not been found.[8]

The satisfactory explanation is found in Genesis. It would

[8]Weisz, p. 721.

appear that at the time of creation God brought into existence organisms fully formed, with all the parts and abilities needed to carry on life in the habitat into which He placed them.

It is interesting to note the "missing links" between the largest groups or phyla. There are also unbridged gaps between the classes and orders and within these groups themselves. Gaps, unfilled by plants or animals, are one of the chief weaknesses of the theory of organic evolution.

In your thinking, digress for a minute and consider the miracle of chlorophyll. What is the possibility that it could have been produced by a long gradual process, being retained and changed over centuries until it reached the place of being useful? Someone has said that it is easier to imagine how life began than it is to imagine how photosynthesis began! Aside from the creative hand of God there is no way to explain it on a materialistic basis. The BSCS biology book, Green Version, gives a very unsatisfactory explanation and says that "somehow, photosynthesis must have started."

It is easier and more logical to think that chlorophyll was miraculously created in a fully developed form ready to start its food-producing function. The same is true of other complex substances such as hemoglobin, enzymes and hormones. It really is not a digression to think about these substances for the absence of a forerunner of them leaves a very definite "missing link."

Note one more thing about the Cambrian rocks. If the theory of organic evolution were true, most of it would have had to take place before the Cambrian. Of the animals that existed then, both simple and complex, representatives of all of the major groups are found living today. "On the phylum level, every group in existence in the Cambrian, has persisted to the present."[9] Note that it is not only the complex organisms that persist, but still found alive are the sim-

[9]*Ibid.*, p. 722.

ple ones that might have been expected to die out. Simple
and complex organisms lived millions of years ago that can
hardly be distinguished from the same kinds of simple and
complex ones of today.

This is surely not evidence for evolution. If that theory
were correct, one would expect to find whole groups of simple ones becoming extinct as they were replaced by newly
evolved ones which were supposed to be better adapted to a
particular set of surroundings. This idea will not always be
found in more advanced works, but in our high school texts
it is usually stated or implied that the animals that did
become extinct did so because ones better fitted to live in a
particular environment evolved and replaced them.

As one thinks back over the Cambrian period, admitting
that we start with the presupposition that God is a Person
who created, certain conclusions are reached. The Cambrian
rocks show many and varied fossils, complex as well as simple. These organisms appear suddenly and with their parts
fully formed. Some of the Cambrian plants and animals,
both simple and complex, have become extinct and some persist today. Of the ones that do persist, some show very little
change whereas others show considerable. However, this
change is all *within* certain major groups and not *between*
the groups. Between the major groups are found many gaps
or "missing links."

Now consider the fossils in the rocks above the Cambrian.
The same quantity of different forms do not appear all at one
time as they do in the Cambrian. Rather there is an ascending succession of appearances, usually each new form dis-
tinctly set apart by a gap from the last and older one. They
do not show an amoeba-to-man picture, and this is to be
expected as it fits in with the creation of various kinds of
animals on the fifth and sixth days of creation. The picture
in general is not one of all things being created at the same
time, but rather of one event following another. About the

animals alone, Genesis 1 says that "God created great whales, and every living creature that moveth, which the waters brought forth abundantly . . . every winged fowl . . . cattle, and creeping thing, and beast of the earth after his kind: and it was so" (Gen. 1:21-24).

If the creation of animals was not instantaneous, but rather one event followed the other, it is reasonable to suppose that the creation of animals within a group also would be done in orderly succession. If God created "fowl that may fly" and later "cattle, and creeping thing and beast," within the former, He may have first created ostrichs, later eagles, and still later owls and sparrows. Each group was told to be fruitful and multiply. Some scientists think that the various kinds of animals did this multiplying to the extent of becoming the dominant form at a certain time. This does not make it necessary to connect a special era or period on the geological time scale with one of the creative days. However, it is known that fish were so predominant during the Devonian period that it is called the Age of Fishes; the Mesozoic era is called the Age of Reptiles; the Cenizoic is known as the Age of Mammals. After their particular period of greatest fruitfulness, as new groups were created, some of the animals from each of these ages became extinct although some persisted and are still living today. The latter, of course, is true of man.

Concerning man, both the Bible and the rocks agree that he was created last. His fossils are found only in the upper crust and he is the highest form of life, for he was made in God's image. As God formed each new group, "gaps" existed between these and ones that He had already created. These gaps show in the fossil record and are recognized by the evolutionist as the chief weakness in his theory. Even Darwin says in the *Origin of Species:*

> Why then is not every geological formation and every stratum full of such intermediate links? Geology as-

suredly does not reveal any such finely-graduated organic chain; and this, perhaps, is the most obvious and
serious objection which can be urged against the theory.[10]
The evolutionary writers of our high school texts recognize
the same weakness. About a large group of plants and animals, they will say, "These suddenly appear in the rocks";
"No forerunner of this organism is known"; "They appeared
as if from nowhere"; "There was a burst of this form." As
was true of the Cambrian period, so also in the more recent
rocks, a complex, fully formed organism suddenly makes its
appearance.

Those who start with a philosophy that allows the miraculous, find this is a perfect picture of each particular thing
being created at a particular time. Those who begin their
thinking with a philosophy prejudiced toward evolution are
left with no satisfactory answer to this most crucial problem.

This discontinuity of the fossil record is one of the glaring
weaknesses of the evolutionary theory. In many people's
thinking this term "missing link" is confined to the link that
could connect man to nonhumans. They think evolution
would be substantiated if this gap were bridged.

It is true that there is very definitely a "missing link" between man and lower animals for man is not just one of the
higher animals. He is different from all others in many ways,
not only in his physical body but also in his spiritual and
mental qualities. However, this is far from being the only
"missing link." Links are missing between and within all the
major plant and animal groups, both in the Cambrian rocks
and throughout the stratigraphic column. If evolution were
true, one would expect to find many connecting links between the different groups, showing some of the changes that
took place by which one organism turned into a different
kind. This would be true whether evolution took place by
many small changes (microevolution) or by fewer but larger

[10]Charles Darwin, *Origin of Species*, Part 2, p. 55.

changes (megaevolution). One would find fossils of plants and animals so intermediate in their form that they could not be classified as belonging to any of the major groups.

Some have thought that a few animals bridge the chasm between two distinctive groups, but such evidence is very scattered and not at all convincing. Even the oldest fossils can usually be readily recognized and be assigned to a classification group.

The Euglena is sometimes called a link between plants and animals. It contains chlorophyll, the green substance used by plants in manufacturing food. One of its chief animal characteristics is the long flagellum which is waved in the water to enable it to quickly swim from place to place. The chief argument, that the Euglena is a link between plants and animals, is the one used in the next paragraph and the one discussed in chapter 3. The argument is "similarity is evidence of relationship," a subjective argument present in the mind of the person doing the studying.

Another animal suggested by the evolutionist to be a connecting link between birds and reptiles is the Archeopteryx. One book says:

> The discovery of the Archeopteryx in Jurassic rock has provided us with one of the best examples of a "missing link." This creature possessed feathers, and thus we may arbitrarily call it a bird. But its relationship to the reptiles is obvious. The rather rudimentary wings had claws. There were teeth in the mouth, and it had a long tail. These are reptilian features no longer in living birds.[11]

Everyone will agree that this interesting animal, long extinct and known only from its fossils, did have these structures. However, in the interpretation of the facts, note several things. First, the quotation shows that the Archeopteryx is linked to the reptiles and the birds on the basis of the argument that "similarity is evidence of relationship." That this is not a valid argument was shown in chapter 3.

[11]Kimball, pp. 610-11.

Second, some feathers of the Archeopteryx are of the most complicated type. If this animal were a connecting link between reptiles and birds this should not be true. On the evolutionary scale, there is an ascending order from simple to complex reptiles and then from simple to complex birds. The connecting link between these two groups of animals should have the characteristics of complex reptiles and simple birds. Instead, the Archeopteroyx has characteristics of the most complex birds! Some of its feathers are of the "most highly" developed type.

A third weakness in reasoning that this animal could be a connecting link between these two groups is the fact that no other animals connect it to a reptilelike ancestry. It suddenly appeared as it is with no indication that it evolved from any other animal. Thus one must conclude that the Archeopteryx was a distinct animal with enough birdlike characteristics to warrant classifying it in that category. Because it became extinct so long ago, it is even more unfamiliar today than recent extinctions like the passenger pigeon and the dodo.

Only the Euglena and the Archeopteryx have been mentioned, but other plants and animals have been suggested as ones that could span the gap between groups of fossils. However, if one studies each of them individually, he will find that each is a separate and distinct organism. That gaps do exist, all evolutionists will agree, but they usually explain the gaps by saying that there are imperfections in the geological record—fossils either were not formed, or have not as yet been found and studied. We do have to agree that the conditions for forming fossils are stringent enough so that we are fortunate to have uncovered as much as we have. Even though this is true, we realize that there are gaps between groups of plants and animals. The evolutionist thinks that these were once filled, thus giving a complete picture from the simple to the complex.

It seems much more reasonable to suppose that the missing links never existed and that the first species in different groups of plants and animals appeared suddenly. We believe that this could have come about only by the creative act of God.

The evolutionist does not believe this and, since gaps in the geological record do exist, he is forced to find some explanation. To fill in the gaps he resorts to the argument "similarity shows relationship." He concludes that if an organism on one side of a gap is similar to that on the other side, the two are related. Of all the information concerning the theory of evolution, the gaps in the geological record are of primary importance. One should expect to find that if one kind of plant or animal had ever changed into another, the evidence of this change would be found in the fossil record. Such convincing evidence is lacking. Not only do the rocks show unbridged gaps between created groups of organisms but they also show "missing links" in the formation of the parts of the plants and animals. Organisms appear in the rocks with all their parts fully formed. As they first appear, such things as wings, arms, legs and eyes are found to be developed, functioning and useful. That this could have happened by chance does not seem reasonable. However, the evolutionist reasons:

> The form of argumentation which takes recourse to purposes and supernatural planning is generally called *teleology*. . . . Clearly, this and all other forms of teleology "explain" an end state by simply asserting it given at the beginning. . . . Care must therefore be taken in scientific endeavors not to fall unwittingly into the teleological trap. . . . The scientifically useful alternative to teleology is called causalism. It has its foundations in mechanistic philosophy. Causalism denies foreknowledge of terminal states, preordination, purposes, goals and fixed fates.[12]

[12]Weisz, pp. 14-15.

This paragraph could have been put under the heading
Evolutionary Interpretation for that is what it is. After reading it, we need to repeat, If a person works within a framework that excludes the miraculous, his conclusions will be
different from those of a person who takes these for granted.
To believe in supernatural purpose and planning we feel is
no "teleological trap." We acknowledge that we do believe
in the supernatural, but we also try to be accurate in our
science. There are certain things that must be taken by faith
by either the evolutionist or the creationist. Of course, the
evolutionist will not call it faith. We accept the verse "By
faith we perceive that the universe was fashioned by the
Word of God, so that the visible came forth from the invisible" (Heb. 11:3, NEB). There is a way in which our faith
is not blind because we have seen the truth of God's Word
in other areas. We have seen lives changed by belief in the
Bible's promises concerning the new birth, and we have seen
and are seeing fulfilled prophecy. It is very easy to move
from these areas of the known to the unknown and so have
faith in a supernatural creation that cannot be explained by
human wisdom. Nevertheless we continue our study of
created things, trying to be objective but not dogmatic when
we propose an interpretation of the facts. The rocks and the
fossils are the facts, but to interpret the history of the past
based on these necessarily involves theories or interpretation.

Before closing this chapter one other thing will be considered that concerns such simple organisms as viruses, bacteria, protozoa and fungi. It has been mentioned that they
existed as far back as there is record of any living things and
also that the same kinds exist today. Some of these simple
forms reproduce every few hours and many things about
their lives can be controlled in the laboratory. The evolutionist usually says that long periods of time, involving large
numbers of generations, are needed for the process of evolution to take place. These simple organisms have provided

these conditions. Since men have been doing experimental work in laboratories under conditions that they can regulate, thousands of generations of these simple plants and animals have had time to reproduce. New hybrids, varieties, strains and other kinds of change are seen, but not evolution in the sense in which we are using the word. The summary of our conclusions regarding the interpretation of the facts of paleontology and geology is this: there is good evidence for thinking that the earth, the rocks and the fossils are very old, having been formed millions and even billions of years ago. The position of the creationist and biblical interpretation *allow* this, and it seems unwise to deny the evidence of great age just because the theory of evolution *necessitates* long time periods.

In addition to the older methods of dating the rock strata and fossils, the more accurate radioactive tests are being used more frequently. When at all feasible, more than one dating method is used on a particular sample. The preponderance of evidence makes it seem reasonable to accept a date of four to five billion years ago for the creation of the earth. We also conclude that the creation of one-celled plants and animals may have been during the Precambrian period, but they surely were well established in the Cambrian, along with representatives of the major groups. In rock layers that form a vertical column above the Cambrian, we find strata with fossils arranged in the order in which it appears that God created them. Both the Bible and science agree that water life was formed first and that various forms of plant and animal life appeared progressively, with man being created last. Since their creation, living things have descended with considerable modification, some having become extinct after having had an age of dominance. This is in harmony with both the facts of science and the biblical account of creation.

5

A Horse Is a Horse

Evolutionary Interpretation

THE STORY OF THE HORSE is especially interesting in view of the fact that it is used as evidence for evolution by all the texts being examined. Most of them give illustrations showing the difference between the fossil remains of an animal called Eohippus and the horse of today. Here is the typical story as given in the BSCS Green Version:

> The earliest organism that can be identified as a member of the family was an Eocene animal scarcely larger than a fox terrier. It had a short muzzle and low-crowned teeth and was a browsing animal. It had four toes on each front foot and three on each hind foot, each toe with a tiny hoof. In comparison with the modern horse, its brain was poorly developed, too—even when allowance is made for the difference in body size. The modern horse has a long muzzle, with a wide gap between the front and rear teeth. Its teeth are high-crowned and well covered with cement, a fine adaptation for grazing on the coarse, dry grasses of the prairie. On each foot it has only one toe, which ends in a large hoof. There are many other differences between the Eocene and the modern horse. The fossil record shows that all these differences are the result of a series of gradual changes. . . . Each change that became established through natural selection must have been very slight.[1]

[1]Biological Science Curriculum Study, *High School Biology, BSCS Green Version*, pp. 594-95.

Most of the books either say or imply that some mutations showed better adaptations than existing ones and therefore had a selective advantage. Vance and Miller express this in one sentence when they say: "Natural selection guided the direction of their evolution which was brought about by gene mutation."[2]

The account in each of the books is very similar. Each gives the age of Eohippus as either fifty or sixty million years. All but two of the books put this section about the horse in a chapter clearly labeled as dealing with evolution. Most of the books arrange their pictures as a series increasing in size— from the small Eohippus to the large horse of today. All the books include some pictures of the toes and legs and most of them also picture the teeth and skulls.

CREATIONIST INTERPRETATION

It is hard for the creationist to be definite in dealing with the fossils of the horse, for one is not working with precise facts as much as with greater or lesser probabilities. In Christian circles there are several schools of thought and the author suggests two to challenge you to study in this area.

As stated, this is not dealing with precise facts, but perhaps it could be said that it is dealing with the interpretation of these facts. Facts do exist, for many horse and horselike skeletons have been found and are in museums to be studied. The problem is to determine how the facts connected with them are to be interpreted. The question is how much change is shown, for we are convinced that they do show change. However, the change is only within a major group or subgroup and so does not show true organic or materialistic evolution. It is not the kind of change by which one major group could ever become another major group.

Several times in this book we note that we have seen in the past, are seeing today and expect to see in the future,

[2]B. B. Vance and D. F. Miller, *Biology for You*, p. 530.

considerable change within groups. Some kinds of change or diversification, less than that seen in horses, may be found in dogs. This diversification has given us Great Danes and tiny poodles, huge St. Bernards and small Pomeranians. Man has greatly increased this change in size and appearance through selective breeding.

As noted, there are various schools of thought concerning the horse. Without being dogmatic about it, the more liberal majority feel that there is good reason to believe that the series of skeletons shown in most high school textbooks is quite reliable. As discovered in the rock strata in many places in the world, the series of horse skeletons seems to show an increase in general size, or at least enough change so that a great variety exists. However, one would be cautious at this point, along with Weisz who makes this qualifying statement about his series of pictures that show an increase in size: "Note, however, that the animals shown represent a selected series and it should not be inferred that horse evolution followed a straight line pattern."[3] He also inserts the idea that the usual series that is pictured does not show all of the horses that may have existed. In this connection, most people would agree that some horses are offshoots from the main line of development.

Some who feel that the ancient horse was the ancestor of the modern horse go one step farther as indicated in Figure 3. They feel that an interpretation of Genesis allows room not only for all horses to have come from one kind, but also for the ass and zebra, and some would even include more animals as possible ancestors.

Other scientists are much more conservative. They are convinced that these animals are not a series either in time or in space. Some think that within the "horse series" there may be three, four or even five separately created kinds. But Genesis says, "Beast of the earth . . . cattle . . . every thing

3P. B. Weisz, *The Science of Biology*, p. 745.

that creepeth . . . fish of the sea, and . . . fowl of the air"
(Gen 1:25-26). Nature does not indicate it, nor does the
written Word imply that God separately created each of the
hundreds of thousands of distinct species. The implication
of the Bible is rather that He created groups. Fossils, as of
the horse, and even activity that is going on at the present
time would indicate this to be true.

Even an evolutionary scientist of considerable stature like
G. Kerkut says in his *Implications of Evolution:* "There are
several puzzling things in the account of the horse." He
continues: "At present, however, it is a matter of faith that
the textbook pictures are true, or even that they are the best
representations of the truth that are available to us at the
present time."[4] This is why men are continually studying to
try to supplement our knowledge in this area.

Another weakness in using the horse series as evidence for
evolution is the fact that there is no known ancestor for even
the most ancient kind of horse. The earliest representations
of the group appear suddenly as fully formed complex organisms. Except for the present-day Equus, all of our study must
be done from fossils and that does not make the work any
easier.

Because the books being used are written for the high
school level, the technical names for the first animals that
could be said to really belong to the horse kind are not considered. However, the fossils show that back of this first horse
kind is a gap. There has been no actual transformation or
production of entirely new forms. Whenever there are gaps,
such as those that appear at places in the horse series, many
conclude that God performed a special creative act.

In this chapter two points of view concerning the horse
are presented. This is a good illustration to show that all
questions are not settled in the minds of creationists. There
is still room for *your* study in many areas. Our conclusion

[4]G. Kerkut, *Implications of Evolution,* p. 148.

about the horse is that it does show change, but this is diversification that does not fall within our definition of evolution.
Then too this is a genealogy that presents many difficulties.
No one should be disturbed by change or diversification that
has taken place in horses anymore than about the change that
has taken place within other groups of plants and animals.
The reason that it disturbs some people may be because the
change in horses is usually given by the evolutionist as an
argument as evidence for his theory. It should *not* be, but
the one idea is usually associated with the other. Some people think, therefore, that because they repudiate evolution
they must also repudiate the diversification seen in the horse,
whether it be much or little.

More is said on this subject in chapter 17. However, until
you read chapter 17 and realize that we are constantly seeing
change in the world of plants and animals, realize that this
change is not true evolution. Even if given an infinite amount
of time, it is not the *kind* of change that could cause one
major group to become another.

6

Is Classification Evidence for Evolution?

EVOLUTIONARY INTERPRETATION

ANOTHER TYPE OF OBSERVATION suggested as evidence for evolution is found in the field of classification. Since this is a variation of the idea that similarity shows relationship, review chapter 3 because a good understanding of it is essential to a real grasp of what follows. The argument states that living things are classified into groups that show similarity; the nearer alike they are the closer they are related in their evolutionary ancestry. Gregory and Trump put this argument into the words of a typical evolutionary text:

> Darwin's theory provided a completely logical basis for classifying living things. If we accept the idea that all life came from simpler forms, it is useful to try to discover which forms came earlier. This suggests the establishment of family trees, relating present organisms to their ancestors. It also leads to the arrangement of the large groups of plants and animals in the order of their probable appearance on earth. Darwin's theory has furnished the most logical basis for classification that we have yet discovered.[1]
>
> Members of the same species are closely related. . . . Similar species, having evolved from a common ancestral population, are grouped together in a *genus.* Similar *genera,* with a more remote common ancestor, are placed in the same *family.* By extending this plan, similar families make up an *order;* similar orders make up a *class;*

[1]W. H. Gregory and E. H. Goldman, *Biological Science,* pp. 96-97.

and similar classes make up a *phylum.* The highest category is a *kingdom,* which is composed of similar phyla.[2]
The fact that plants and animals may be classified into groups
such as this, is said to be evidence that they developed in
the same way. The evolutionist says that a maple tree and
a man have very little in common because their common
ancestors existed in very remote geological time. The common ancestors of a frog and a man are not so far back in
history, so they are nearer alike, and the ancestors of a man
and an ape would be even more recent. It is not argued that
man came from the ape but rather that somewhere in the
past they had a common ancestor. This ancestry was more
recent than that shared with the maple tree or the frog and
therefore they have more likenesses.

CREATIONIST INTERPRETATION

Everyone agrees that living things can be classified. The
terms given above are the ones generally used by evolutionist
and creationist alike. Let us see how they apply to a couple
of animals and a plant.

KINGDOM	Animal	Animal	Plant
PHYLUM	Chordata	Chordata	Tracheophyta
CLASS	Mammalia	Mammalia	Angiospermae
ORDER	Primate	Carnivora	Malvales
FAMILY	Hominidae	Canidae	Tiliaceae
GENUS	Homo	Canis	Tilia
SPECIES	sapiens	familaris	americana
COMMON NAME	Man	Dog	Linden Tree

All of the high school texts being used give classification as
evidence that evolution has taken place. As seen in the
quotations above, this conclusion is often specifically stated.
Some advanced books do not even mention that classification
can be used as evidence for evolution because this is a weak
argument. If one is honest, he has to agree that it is evidence
neither for nor against evolution or creation. In either case
plants and animals are taken as found, and working with

[2]R. F. Trump and D. E. Fagle, *Design for Life,* p. 433.

what is given, one proceeds to classify them. Every day the same thing is done in sorting our kinds of money, stamps, buildings, furniture and even the words in a dictionary. For example, money could be divided into paper and metal. Coins could then be subdivided into ones that are more alike on the basis of size, value or kind of metal from which they are made. The fact that ones that show special likenesses are put into certain groups does not necessarily indicate that they came one from the other. Neither does it show that the same person designed them, although this might well be true.

The modern system of classification of living things has developed gradually over the past centuries. Some of the first work was done by Aristotle in the fourth century B.C., but it was not until the middle of the eighteenth century that Carl Linnaeus gave us many of the basic principles used today. It is an important concept and a way of systematizing biological knowledge. Although it is a very useful and necessary branch of biology, it is of little value as an argument for evolution, and the author agrees with Trump that "it is a manmade scheme,"[3] and with Gregory that "there is no classification in nature."[4] The use of this argument as evidence for evolution is one that goes around in a circle. The evolutionist concludes that evolution has taken place because things can be classified into categories, and then he says that classification is possible because things have evolved one from the other! He starts with the assumption that his theory is true and bases his conclusion on that assumption. This idea is better used as an argument for design. Plants and animals are similar because God created them that way. He used the same general plan for a number of different organisms, rather than each individual being created different from any other. The author agrees with the scientists who realize that an argument from classification is not true scientific evidence.

[3]*Ibid.*, p. 447.
[4]Gregory and Goldman, p. 96.

7

Significance of the Evidence from Biochemistry

EVOLUTIONARY INTERPRETATION

ANOTHER ARGUMENT presented by the evolutionist as evidence for his theory is found in the field of biochemistry. It is stated that genetic relationship is shown where resemblances are seen in the composition and action of various substances and secretions of living organisms. A number of kinds of substances are given in the various books with the conclusion that evolution from a common ancestor is the best way of accounting for these likenesses. For instance:

> Is it not remarkable that all living things should use nucleic acids, and most of them a particular nucleic acid, DNA, for the vehicle of heredity? Is it not equally a sign of relationship that all organisms use ATP for energy transfers, or that almost all plants use chlorophyll for photosynthesis?[1]

A few authors indicate that they think embryos show biochemical recapitulation. Kimball says that while a chick is developing inside the shell, its waste materials show the stages through which its ancestors have evolved. It first passes through an ammonia-excreting stage (reminiscent of a fish), then a urea-excreting stage (reminiscent of an amphibian), and finally a uric-acid stage which exists when the chick hatches. "This certainly suggests that the chick is repeating stages in the biochemical development of its ancestors."[2]

[1]Biological Science Curriculum Study, *Biological Science: An Inquiry into Life*, Yellow Version, p. 607.
[2]J. W. Kimball, *Biology*, p. 547.

Another author gives this same account of the chick in almost the same words. He also includes it under the heading "The Evidence From Comparative Biochemistry."[3] In advanced texts this material might be included in a chapter on embryology, but we are putting it under the heading of biochemistry since this is what is done in the high school books being used. The same is true of other material in this chapter.

Another line of investigation in this field concerns enzymes and hormones. Enzymes such as pepsin and trypsin are found occurring throughout the animal kingdom. The hormone thyroxin is found in all vertebrates. Kimball says:

> Evolution from a common ancestor provides the only satisfactory explanation for the presence of the same hormone in different vertebrates. . . . Thus we have . . . a hormone inherited from a common ancestor but with its functions modified in ways appropriate to the life of each animal.[4]

Another author draws the same conclusion, "Fossils seem to show that mammals are descended from a common ancestor and are closely related to each other."[5] He says that this is shown by the fact that their digestive enzymes are much alike, thyroid from a sheep can be used by humans and insulin from a pig is used by man.

The most common argument in this field concerns serology and blood tests as given in several books. The classical work tells how human blood serum is injected into a rabbit. This injection causes the rabbit to produce immune bodies or antibodies. The serum then taken from the rabbit is called antihuman serum because it will react against human serum. It is useful in criminal cases to test even a very small quantity of material to see if it is human blood.

The evolutionist uses this serum in tests called precipitation tests. When antihuman serum is mixed with the serum

[3]C. A. Villee, *Biology*, p. 612.
[4]Kimball, p. 547.
[5]E. Kroeber, W. H. Wolff and R. L. Weaver, *Biology*, p. 483.

of many animals, a white precipitate is formed. The varying amounts of this precipitate are said to show the degree of evolutionary relationship between these animals. The more precipitate formed, the closer the animal is said to be related to man. Kimball gives a chart listing the "reaction between antihuman precipitations (prepared in rabbit) and the serum of various mammals, with human taken as 100 percent." Some samples from his table list the gorilla as 64 percent; orangutan, 42 percent; baboon, 29 percent; dog, 3 percent; and the horse, 2 percent. "The amount [of precipitate] produced decreases, however, from man to horse . . . this corresponds closely to the presently accepted degree of kinship between man and these other mammals."[6]

In this same area, the following is an interesting quotation concerning the work of Johannes Kylstra from *Life* magazine: "Human beings are animals evolved from the salt sea, and human blood is much closer in composition to sea water than to fresh water."[7]

CREATIONIST INTERPRETATION

As you think over what has been said in the previous chapters, what would be your conclusion concerning the validity of this argument? Do you see how it is based on one assumed premise? This premise states that similarity shows degree of relationship and this is evidence of evolutionary descent. It was said that this argument would be referred to a number of times. Here it is under another guise. Review again the material in chapter 3 where a number of points are given that could account for the fact that likenesses can be seen in many plants and animals. As similarities are seen in their anatomy and embryos, so one would expect to see the same basic chemical composition used for such things as the protoplasm from which they are made, and for their hor-

[6]*Ibid.*, pp. 547-48.
[7]"A Mouse Breathes Liquids—and Lives," *Life* magazine, Vol. LXIII, No. 8 (August 25, 1967), p. 78.

mones and enzymes.

It is not to his credit that, especially in this field where admitted likenesses are found, the evolutionist seems to have selected for his use that material which shows the point he is trying to make, and disregards the other facts. In this connection it is often cited that blood tests can be used to show that human beings are not related one to the other. If, without proper testing and selection, blood is transfused between people of antagonistic blood types, fatal results may occur. This can be true even among people in the same family. Because their blood is incompatible, one can neither assume that they are not related nor that they are not members of the human race. In this case, instead of similarity being evidence of relationship, dissimiliarity appears where there is a known close kinship.

In the same way there are other types of blood reactions that point to a close relation between animals that are very different structurally. To make this even clearer, let us set up a hypothetical situation. Use the five animals listed previously—gorilla, orangutan, baboon, dog and horse. Literally dozens of substances in their bodies could be chemically analyzed and the percentages of likeness to man could be put into table form.

First use the antihuman serum as already described. Then determine the acidity of the stomach, the salt content of the blood, the percentage of iron in the hemoglobin, the amount of phosphorus in the protoplasm, the exact percentage of calcium in the blood—one could go on and on. As each test is run, tabulate the results, and then study and compare them one with the other.

All the results will not be the same, as was found with the antihuman serum. Instead of showing that the gorilla is closest to the human and the horse the farthest away, the order within the tables will be varied and there might be all possible kinds of combinations. If one wanted to show some special relationship between these five animals, he might present only the tables that substantiated his theory. Selecting only certain facts for presentation seems to have been done in this field of biochemistry.

Some very early tests were the previously mentioned blood-serum tests and they showed the results as have been given. They found their way into secondary school texts about fifty years ago and have stayed there ever since. Specific figures as determined by biochemical tests that have been made in recent years are seldom mentioned in high school books.

In conclusion, keep in mind the fact that God seems to have used a basic plan in creation and allowed diversity to meet specific needs.

First, for this reason one does find some biochemical likenesses throughout the plant and animal kingdom. This can be seen in many places. For example, most plants contain chlorophyll; all living things contain nucleic acid (most of them the particular nucleic acid DNA used for the vehicle of heredity), and use ATP for energy transfer and RNA to direct protein synthesis.

Second, consider again that God could have made each of the over half a million different kinds of plant and a million kinds of animal entirely unique. The fact that He has used some similarities in basic construction in no way argues for evolution or against a common Designer.

Last, it is important to note that specific amounts of chemicals present, and figures gathered from the way materials react one with the other, give such contradictory results that they are not safe guides to use in discovering relationships. Even human blood transfusions may cause death if the donor and recipient are of different blood types.

Summarizing, let us state that one is not justified in regarding chemical resemblance as a good basis for establishing relationships in the sense of living organisms having common ancestry.

8

Trouble with Geographic Distribution

WHY ARE KANGAROOS found only in and around Australia? Why are llamas only in South America? Why are there no bears in Africa and no elephants in North America? Questions such as these must be honestly and seriously considered by both the evolutionist and by those who do not accept the theory. It takes very little discernment to observe that some plants and animals are found only in certain places on the earth's surface. The reasons for this uneven geographic distribution present a real problem. This problem has no easy solution, but it is interesting to study and to search for explanations.

EVOLUTIONARY INTERPRETATION

It really makes little difference whether under this heading or under "Creationist Interpretation" some differences are cited between living things that are related to their geographic distribution. The location of these plants and animals is factual material with which one must agree. A parting of the ways comes when the evolutionist says, "Evolution explains quite naturally . . . the seemingly strange distribution of some of the plants and animals on the earth."[1]

Most of the books being examined devote considerable space to the discussion of geographic distribution, and the following illustrations are taken from their texts:

> Changes that result from geographic isolation occur very slowly, often requiring millions of years. At least

[1] E. Kroeber, W. H. Wolff and R. L. Weaver, *Biology*, p. 486.

one case, however, has been documented in fairly recent times. During the 15th century, a few European rabbits were introduced into the Madeiras, islands off the west coast of Africa. Today, their descendants are smaller and darker than their recent ancestors. But far more important than their physical appearance is the fact that they can no longer be mated with the European species. So great has been the change that they are now considered a separate species.[2]

The distribution of cottontail rabbits in this country provides still another example of the role played by geographic isolation in the formation of species. In the eastern half of our country, only eight species are found, while in the mountainous western states there are 23. In this case, high mountains provided geological isolation as effective as the ocean waters.[3]

On the north rim of the Grand Canyon in northern Arizona a familiar mammal of the yellow pine forests is the Kaibab squirrel. It has long tufted ears, dark underparts, and a whitish tail. Across the mile-wide canyon, on the south rim, the Abert squirrel is at home in the yellow pines. Much like the squirrels of the north rim, the Abert squirrels have the same distinctively shaped ears; but their underparts are much lighter, their tails slightly darker. . . . Although these squirrels live in close geographic association, they are separated by the Colorado River. Because of their isolation, two closely related species have evolved.[4]

The evolutionist explains the distribution of the marsupials in the following way:

After islands are separated from the mainland, their animal populations become isolated from their ancestral stock. In time, they may become strikingly dif-

[2]W. H. Gregory and E. H. Goldman, *Biological Science*, p. 707.
[3]J. W. Kimball, *Biology*, p. 569.
[4]R. F. Trump and D. L. Fagle, *Design for Life*, pp. 419-20.

ferent as they become adapted to a different environment.

This difference is dramatically illustrated by the animals of Australia and Tasmania. These islands are practically the only places in the world where the pouched mammals, the *marsupials,* are native. This results from the fact that Australia and Tasmania were separated from the Asiatic mainland before the placental mammals developed. On the islands, the marsupials continued to exist unhampered by competition from the more aggressive placentals that appeared on the mainland. On the mainland, the marsupials disappeared, probably killed off by the flesh-eating placentals.[5]

This text then goes on to say that in the Australian area are found animals evolved only as far as the marsupials, whereas on other continents the animals continued to evolve on up into the greater variety of nonpouched animals seen today. The evolutionists say that they had long been perplexed by the distribution of plants and animals but that explanations such as this have "solved the puzzle."

The BSCS Yellow Version text gives an account of the red fox in North America. It produces a mutation resulting in the beautiful silver fox. Red and silver hairs mingled, giving what trappers call a cross fox. In North America the silver type is by far the commonest in the north, the red fox in the south, and the cross fox in between. This geographic distribution seems to be related to natural selection, for the silver fox is less conspicuous when hunting its prey across the snow in the north, and the red fox is less conspicuous when hunting in the woods and meadows in areas where there is foliage.

CREATIONIST INTERPRETATION

As is noted in other places in this book, it is not the facts with which one disagrees, but rather the interpretation of these facts. When considering this subject, as with others,

[5]Gregory and Goldman, p. 707.

the thinking of the evolutionist is influenced toward the theory of organic evolution because he has ruled out miraculous creation.

Concerning geographic distribution, both the evolutionist and the creationist observe the same facts. The illustrations given are examples of hundreds that exist. Both the evolutionist and the creationist note that certain plants and animals are limited to certain continents (as the kangaroo), to certain islands (as the rabbits on the Madeiras), or to certain smaller areas (as the Kaibab and Abert squirrels near the Grand Canyon). These same animals may be conspicuously absent from very similar continents, islands, and areas.

In general, living things tend to spread out from a single location. If they are able to pass along a geographic corridor, they move out to places that have suitable climate and food supply and do not have too many enemies. Eventually they may come to a barrier, such as bodies of water, mountains or deserts, that will stop most of them. A few plants or animals out of a large group may be able to cross the barrier. For example, a dandelion seed might be carried by the wind across a mountain barrier; an insect might cross a desert riding on the back of a bird; a small animal might be taken across a lake on a log; or a bird might fly farther than usual across a stretch of ocean.

Suppose that two animals happen to cross some particular mountain and settle down to make it their home. The animals on both sides of the barrier, in this case the mountain, have the same ancestry but they are now separated from each other. As the two now-isolated groups continue to grow and reproduce, differences will become noticeable. Those on one side of the mountain will produce mutations and hybrids, and recombinations and translocations of their genes will occur. Different kinds of mutations and other changes will take place on the other side of the barrier. Gradually the two populations will develop differences. These differences are seen in the examples that have already been given for foxes, marsupials, rabbits and squirrels. Examples from all over the world would extend the list almost limitlessly.

Barriers that cause these differences are usually pictured as being something physical, but sometimes a physiological difference or a behavior pattern may become a barrier that will isolate a segment of a population. Experiments have been made in which young salmon from a particular stream have been captured, tagged and then released. Later these same salmon, now grown to maturity after having lived in the ocean along with salmon from other streams, have been recaptured in the very streams where they had hatched. However, no tagged ones were found in adjoining streams. The salmon from the various rivers had been mixed together in the ocean but those from a particular stream had remained separate and distinct as far as their breeding habits were concerned. Because of this isolation caused by a behavior pattern, differences have arisen between fish that spawn in different streams.

Some problems connected with the irregular distribution of living things are closely tied in with what we call land bridges. At some time in the past, bridges of land that are now separated from each other, were undoubtedly connected, and vice versa. Evidence indicates that North and South America were not connected in the past. We also think that Asia and North America were once connected through the Bering Strait. The whole subject of geographical distribution contains many unsolved problems, but in most cases we have to take into account the fact that bodies of land and water were not always connected the way we now see them. This fact helps solve some problems but creates others! One of these involves the marsupials.

The marsupial is one of the orders of the class Mammalia. The young are born in a very immature condition and cling to a milk gland in the pouch of the mother until they develop enough to be able to shift for themselves.

We are most familiar with the kangaroo and opossum but this group also includes such others as the koala bear, wallaby, the Tasmanian wolf and Tasmanian devil (much like the wolf and badger of North America), the wombat (similar to a woodchuck), and the phalangers (resembling squirrels).

On the evolutionary scale the marsupials are "lower" than the placental mammals whose young are born in a much more mature condition, having been nourished through the placenta. Most of the marsupials are found in the Australian area although the opossum is native to North America. To say that in Australia animals evolved up only as far as the marsupials, while on other continents they evolved farther into all the kinds of placential mammals we see today, does not "solve the puzzle" for us. The fossil evidence indicates, and it seems reasonable to suppose, that the first marsupials were created after their kind as the biblical record indicates. Geographical distribution and different environmental conditions are factors that help explain some of the variety of marsupials existing today. However, as the title of this chapter indicates, problems still exist and there are still questions to be answered. Christian scientists are continually studying to try to determine how much diversification there has been from the created kind.

It is largely from a study of the fossils that scientists can determine how much change there has been. Wherever one sees an unbridged structural gap between groups of plants or animals (in this case marsupials) it seems warranted to come to the conclusion that the first organisms of that group were specially created.

Think over what has been said about changes that result from animals being separated from each other by physical or physiological barriers. Note three points. First, changes that are caused by geographical distribution *do* occur. Hundreds of examples exist, and have been mentioned in connection with foxes, rabbits, squirrels, salmon and marsupials. The second point has to do with the reasons *why* plants and animals, separated from ones that are just like them, gradually develop differences. The third consideration has to do with *how much* change, due to factors connected with their geographical distribution, can be found in organisms.

The last two factors are examined in chapter 9. At this point it should be realized that the place to study the amount of change that has taken place is in the fossils.

When studying backward in the sequence of a series of fossils one may come to a dead end. No ancestor may be found for the particular plant or animal being considered. When a gap exists between two forms of living things and no ancestor for an individual has been found, it should be assumed that God performed a creative act to establish the first one of that particular "kind," or that future research may show a common ancestor. The Bible does not tell us how many or which ones He created. The Bible does tell us that God created things "after their kind," but it does not go into a detailed and scientific account of the "kinds." Nowhere does the Bible define or set the boundaries and limits of these "kinds."

One could make a hodgepodge list of scientific and non-scientific terms such as: species, group, race, genus, individual, family, order, class, subspecies, type, breed and variety. From such a list no person has license to pick one term and only one and say that this is the one "kind" that God created. The Bible does not tell us that He created all the different races, or all the different species, or all of the different families. Certainly the evidence is against His having separately created such individual kinds of cow as the Jersey, Hereford, Aberdeen Angus, Holsteins, Guernseys, Brown Swiss and Shorthorns. It appears that He created a type ancestor from which, by limited change, have developed all these different kinds of cow.

The same reasoning is thought to be true of other classification groups. Many Christian scientists think that evidence points to the fact that He created an ancestral type called a jungle hen. From it, by the use of laws He put into operation, have come the Plymouth Rocks, Bantams, Rhode Island Reds and many other kinds of chickens.

Some people think that the biblical term "kind" should be used synonymously with "species" but this is not necessarily true. The word "species" is a man-made classification term popularized by Linnaeus (1707-78) who devised the system of classification that is still used today. Elsewhere in this book we tell about naming plants and animals by means of a system that uses two Latin names. The first is the genus name and it is usually written with a capital letter. This is followed by the species name, beginning with a lower-case letter. It describes a specific type within the genus. Linnaeus felt that all the species remained the same as when first created, but there were many things about heredity that he did not know. When one of his books was published in 1758 only 4,236 animals were listed. A hundred years later the number had grown to 129,000. Today the number of classified animals is over 900,000 and that of plants over 350,000.[6]

In chapter 17 the mechanism of change in living things is examined. As just noted, living organisms do change. Isolation and barriers are closely connected with the development of various characteristics. This change within the scriptural "kind" is limited, and the boundaries of these limitations are seen in the gaps found in the fossils and among living things.

---

[6]*Ibid.*, pp. 93, 96.

9

Toward an Understanding of Embryology

DURING THE LATEST FEW YEARS a real change has been seen developing in the use of evidence presented in the field of embryology. The change in the point of view is well illustrated in an article in *Life* magazine which gives an excellent series of color photos of the early development of human embryos. In speaking of two bulges in the head of a four-week-old embryo it says:

> The one at left is the lower-jaw-to-be, the other smaller one will be the tiny bone the tongue will be attached to. These structures often resemble "gill arcs" in fish embryos. Some scientists believe this is a leftover from earlier evolution, when our ancestors may have breathed through gill-like organs. Others have lately come around to the less romantic view that this is just the way things happen to look at this stage of embryonic growth.[1]

EVOLUTIONARY INTERPRETATION

Many books we are now considering still present embryological material as evidence of evolution, but some say that it should be viewed with caution. Some books omit the subject.

Young people often like the sound of the phrase "ontogeny recapitulates phylogeny." This means: "The evidence from embryology seems to indicate that each animal in its indi-

[1]"The Drama of Life Before Birth," *Life* magazine, Vol. LVIII, No. 17 (April 30, 1965), p. 58.

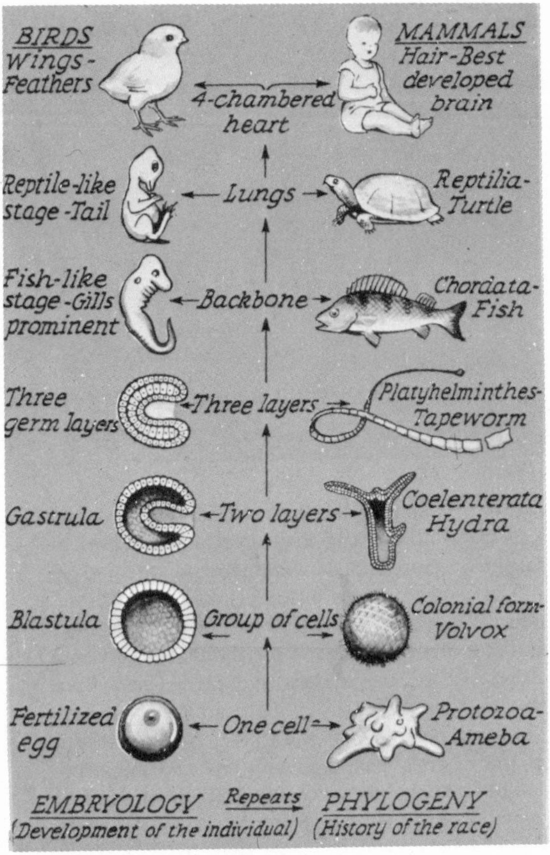

Figure 5

Evidences of Ancestry. The following is the evolutionary explanation: "Each individual passes through stages in its growth and development that are similar to the changes that occurred in the development of the race. Animals still start from a single cell, the simplest form of life in history. Trace the development of the individual (lower left), comparing each step to the historical development of living forms (right)" (from N. M. Smallwood, I. L. Reveley and G. A. Bailey's *Elements of Biology;* revised by Ruth A. Dodge; © Copyright 1959, 1964 by Allyn & Bacon, Inc. Reproduced by permission of Allyn & Bacon, Inc.

vidual development passes through stages which resemble those of its remote ancestors."[2] In other words, it is said that the development of the individual parallels that of the race. Figure 5 shows drawings taken from R. A. Dodge's text *Elements of Biology* to explain the idea pictorially. They show the development of a chick from the fertilized egg, through successively complex embryological stages, and climaxing in the adult. This is paralleled by the supposed development of the race from a one-celled animal to a hydra, to a jelly fish, to a tapeworm, and finally to a man as the most complex and recent organism.

In the case of the human, the changes that take place in the nine months of the gestation period are supposed to be a recapitulation of what took millions of years to accomplish by organic evolution, as single-celled animals became the complex ones of today. In some texts this evolutionary idea is given pictorially as shown in Figure 5.

In the high school books being used there is reference to only two stages through which the embryo is supposed to have passed. These are the one-celled animal and the fishlike creature. A few years ago many books also included a hairy and a tail stage. These have fallen into disrepute and are now usually omitted.

Of the two stages most often mentioned, first think about what is said concerning the one-celled stage. One book says, "The fertilized egg is but a single cell theoretically corresponding to a protozoan."[3] Another says, "The early stages of all vertebrate embryos are remarkably similar and it is not easy to differentiate a human embryo from the embryo of a pig, chick, frog or fish."[4]

The gill slits, the heart and the lungs are mentioned in connection with the fishlike stage. We read, "At one stage the

[2]T. J. Moon, J. H. Otto, and A. Towle, *Modern Biology*, p. 662.
[3]C. J. Goodnight, M. L. Goodnight, and R. R. Armacost, *Biology, An Introduction to the Science of Life*, p. 373.
[4]C. E. Villee, *Biology*, p. 612.

human embryo has gill slits."[5] One book indicates that many mammals had a fishlike ancestry by saying that their embryos had a two-chambered heart and circulatory system like a fish before developing their four-chambered heart. "The comparing of embryos of different animals also shows us that vertebrate lungs have developed from the swim bladder, or air bladder of fishlike animals."[6]

Aside from the brief mention of the one-celled and fishlike stages of the embryo, most other textual material is given simply by calling attention to the general similarity in external appearance. Instead of committing themselves one way or the other in words, most books try to put across their idea in diagrams. Their conclusion is the one seen before—similarity means descent from a common ancestor. One book that has a chart of the diagrams of various embryos says that by looking at them you will see "what puzzled the students of embryology." Without calling attention to any particular likenesses between the various embryos they say that the puzzle has been solved because "naturally organisms that are related show resemblances."[7] This same reasoning is used by Goodnight who says, "The more closely related the animals are the more similar their embryos are."[8]

Most books in their charts of embryonic resemblances show about six stages of four or five animals. The BSCS Blue and Green versions show seven animals with seven stages of each as given in Figure 6.

The whole setup of these drawings is to emphasize resemblances and only the Green Version makes the comment "Drawings are not on the same scale."[9] The Blue Version makes neither interpretations nor conclusions; these are left to the reader. Accompanying its forty-nine drawings of de-

[5]*Ibid.*, p. 373.
[6]Moon, Otto and Towle, *ibid.*
[7]K. Kroeber, W. H. Wolff, and R. L. Weaver, *Biology*, p. 482.
[8]Goodnight, Goodnight and Armacost, *ibid.*
[9]Biological Science Curriculum Study, *High School Biology: BSCS Green Version*, p. 578.

veloping embryos we find only two sentences: "Study [the figures] very carefully. Trace the development of each of these vertebrates and compare their development."[10]

Another method used in an effort to instill the author's preconceived idea about evolution is the use of questions. Since the argument in this field is very weak, a question allows the evolutionist to implant a concept without committing him-

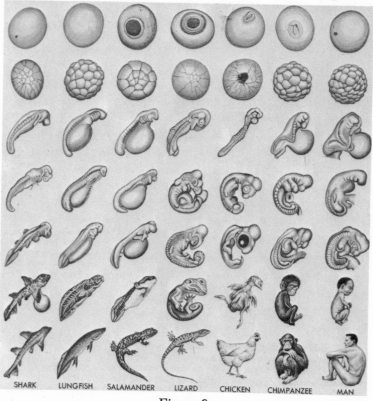

Figure 6

An evolutionary comparison of the development of various vertebrates from the BSCS Blue Version (used by permission of the Biological Science Curriculum Study).

[10]BSCS, *Biological Science: Molecules to Man,* Blue Version, p. 307.

self to an idea that is already outdated. This is the same technique used in courtroom trials by lawyers who know that a certain type of question will be stricken from the record, but they also know that the asking of the question will influence the thinking of the jury to move in the direction they desire. In like manner, accompanying his pictured diagrams, Kroeber asks:

> In what ways are these early embryos alike? In the top row there is still a great resemblance between embryos of reptiles, birds and mammals. In what respects are they similar? At a still later stage, which embryo looks more like the human embryo, the turtle or the pig? . . . Why this similarity?[11]

CREATIONIST INTERPRETATION

Embryology, which traces the development of an egg, is a fascinating subject. If there is any field of biology where supernatural creative power (rather than naturalistic evolution) can be seen at work, it is here. He is truly a miracle-working God who can cause a single cell to develop into a complex animal. From the egg grow various kinds of tissue, organ and system until one sees the perfectly functioning organism. As a creationist approaches the field of embryology, thoughts about the wonders of creation cross his mind. On the other hand, a materialistic evolutionist, because he is working within a different framework, looks at embryology in a different way and finds little to strengthen his theory. A brief consideration will show the fallacies of the evolutionist's line of reasoning.

First, consider the fact that there *is* a resemblance between embryos. However, this is not nearly as striking as the textbook illustrations suggest. If a person had before him the actual embryos instead of the diagrams, he would be able to see more differences than the pictures show.

Ernst Haeckel (1834-1919) made the original series of

[11]Kroeber, Wolff and Weaver, *ibid.*

diagrams to picture this resemblance. Later he admitted that some of his drawings had been intentionally changed to make them fit the theory he was trying to prove. It is said that when confronted with the fact that some of his drawings were not true to life, Haeckel said that he would feel condemned by admitting the fact if it were not that many other scientists had also doctored, schematized and reconstructed their drawings. It would seem as though he were exaggerating in his condemnation of other scientists, but surely he should be able to speak for himself! This is all history now and even the evolutionist recognizes that it was unfortunate.

In speaking about the similarity of embryos, the BSCS Yellow Version says, "Further investigation showed that overzealous artistry had indicated a few resemblances that did not quite exist!"[12] Of Haeckel's work, Weisz says, "His views are now largely discredited, but they were once so influential that many of them still persist today under various guises."[13]

Ever since Haeckel's original schematization, books have continued to picture various embryos, most emphasizing such similarities as size and curvature. Everyone will admit that similarities exist, especially in the early stages of embryos, but there is not nearly as much as these pictures would lead us to believe.

Not only do persons disagree about the degree of likeness, but they also put a different interpretation on the facts. As noted in other places in this book, the argument that similarity indicates relationship can also be interpreted as indicating a common Designer. If the one who studies this subject has a belief in God, he can see here the Creator's hand at work. Just because two animals or two embryos look something alike does not mean that they came from a common ancestor anymore than it is evidence that they were patterned after a common plan in the mind of God.

[12]BSCS, *Biological Science: An Inquiry into Life: Yellow Version*, p. 608.
[13]P. B. Weisz, *The Science of Biology*, p. 732.

In saying that there are some resemblances among embryos, it should also be added that they are mostly superficial
—each embryo invariably develops into the kind of individual
that produced the egg. Chicken eggs develop into chickens
and frog eggs into frogs. The best way to see how different
embryos really are is to let them grow, each into its characteristic form. But consider the meaning of some of the likenesses. For example, blood-vessel patterns appear in some
embryos and then are replaced by the ones that are seen in
the animal at the time of birth or hatching. Rather than looking at these blood vessels as recapitulation, is it not more
reasonable to suppose that they serve some useful purpose as
the embryo grows in an orderly way into an increasingly complex organism? Much more is to be learned in this connection
but present knowledge does not allow us to say that these
parts are useless or just historical remnants of past ancestors.

God could have made a different pattern for each developing animal but He was not obliged to do so. If some general
plan of growth was satisfactory, He could have used that
common plan over and over again. By changing the word
"evolution" to "Creator" we would agree with the general
idea as given in the BSCS Yellow Version which says, "Evolution tends to be a conservative process. Rather than develop structures anew, it tends to remodel existing ones."[14]
It has been well said that the Creator tends to be conservative. Rather than develop structures anew, He tends to remodel ones from a few general basic plans that He uses.
Rather than accept the recapitulation theory, we may look at
temporary embryonic structures as either (1) having some
function in the developing embryo, and/or (2) being part
of a creative plan modified to fit the needs of each particular
animal.

The proposition that human individuals begin life as one-
celled protozoans is misleading. They begin life as a fer-

[14]BSCS, Yellow Version, p. 607.

tilized human ovum or egg, which is very different in structure and function from a one-celled animal. This fertilized ovum is capable of developing into a new individual, but it can neither reproduce itself nor carry on many of the life processes that are found in a protozoan. Life has to start in the simplest form, an egg, and then by repeated cell division it gradually develops. The fact that this simplest form is one-celled and that a protozoan is one-celled does not mean that one is ancestral to the other. As *Life* magazine says, "This is just the way things happen to look at this stage of embryonic growth."[15] We see no basis for accepting this recapitulation part of the evolutionary theory.

A few years ago some books discussed the "gills" of human embryos. However, this idea was so obviously not the case that the teaching now usually refers to the "gill slits" only. But this, too, is misleading. As the embryo develops, there are ridges that grow in from the side and develop into parts of the tongue, lower jaw and neck. Although there are folds between these ridges, they do not function in respiration. As the embryo grows older the ridges are incorporated into parts of the face and neck as mentioned in the *Life* quotation. The depressions between these ridges do not break through into the pharynx and are not really comparable to the gill slits of a fish.

Kimball is one of the few authors who still states that the human embryo has "temporary possession of a tail."[16] Instead of talking about a tail, authors are usually speaking of the coccyx or end part of the backbone. To be a tail, a structure must be a caudal appendage with its own muscles, nerves and blood supply. The coccyx, found in the human embryos, is not a separate and distinct structure having these characteristics but is merely the terminal portion of the backbone. After all, it does have to have an end!

[15]"The Drama . . . ," *ibid.*
[16]W. J. Kimball, *Biology*, p. 545.

It is true that at one time in the developing embryo the coccyx projects beyond the surrounding parts because it has a faster rate of growth than these other parts. However, that never makes it anything other than the end of the backbone. An exception is mentioned in chapter 10 concerning vestigial structures.

Several unanswered questions are in the whole line of reasoning in the field of embryology. If the developing embryo is supposed to reenact stages in the history of the race, why are so few stages included? How can such stages as the larva and pupa of an insect be explained? Why are recapitulation stages supposed to be seen in only a few parts of the embryo whereas other parts do not show this? Why are the changes in a developing plant embryo considered to be of little significance? There are so many unanswered questions and so many problems in this area that more and more scientists are recognizing the weaknesses of offering material from this field as evidence for evolution. Even though written from the evolutionary point of view, the BSCS Yellow Version says, "Today the idea of embryonic resemblance is viewed with caution . . . the old idea that a human passes through a fish, amphibian and reptile stage during early development is not correct."[17]

Weisz is a thoroughgoing evolutionist and yet he discredits the fact that evidence for the theory can be found in this idea of embryonic recapitulation. Pointing at a number of objections, he says, "The conclusion is certainly warranted that recapitulation . . . simply does not occur."[18] We agree with this summation.

[17]BSCS, Yellow Version, p. 608.
[18]Weisz, p. 733.

10

Of Use or Not of Use?

EVOLUTIONARY INTERPRETATION

ANOTHER FIELD from which the evolutionist suggests evidence for his theory is that of vestigial structures. These parts of the body are generally accepted as being useless and usually are considered remnants left over from a useful state in some ancestral animal. The following quotations sum up this argument:

> Another bit of evidence to show that living things resemble each other is the presence of **vestigial organs**. Why does man have an appendix? Why does the snake have the remnants of hind limb bones and the porpoise pelvic bones? The presence of these and other structures in living things brings man to the conclusion that they descended from ancestors which needed and used these structures.[1]

> Man has an appendix which seems to be of no use and may do harm. Some people have scalp and ear muscles which they can contract, but to no purpose. You have small fused bones at the lower end of your spinal column that form a short tail. The whale has no hind legs, but it has a number of small bones on each side of the spinal column in that region where you would expect hind legs to be attached. If you believe that the different types of animals are related—that they are all descended from some common ancestor or ancestors—you can explain why these useless structures are present. You can con-

[1]R. A. Dodge, *Elements of Biology*, p. 631.

sider them as "remnants" of structures that once were
useful to the ancestor.[2]

During the last few years the weight placed on this argument has been receiving less and less attention in high school
books. Some years ago a list of useless vestigial organs would
have included the thyroid and pituitary glands. It is amazing
to find one high school text with a copyright date as recent as
1965 which says: "In man there are more than two hundred
vestigial structures."[3] What about the books being examined
in this book which are currently used in classrooms? Aside
from this general reference to two hundred vestiges, and another author who says he refers to probably a hundred vestiges, four is the largest number of specific ones listed in any
one text. Besides the human vestiges, there are mentioned
bones where one would expect hind legs on a whale and on
a python, wings on flightless birds like the kiwi and ostrich,
the V-shaped abdomen of the crab, and splints in a horse's
leg.

CREATIONIST INTERPRETATION

The fact that within a few years the number of human vestiges listed by most authorities has dropped from several
hundred to just a few gives us our first tool to use against
this line of reasoning. Learning the functions of parts of our
body has been a continuing process for centuries past. As a
part is studied and its function discovered it is removed from
the list of useless organs. Even the pituitary gland used to be
called vestigial, but it is now known to be of such prime importance that it is frequently called the "master gland."

It has been said that "our list of useless structures decreases
as our store of knowledge increases." Most of these formerly
so-called useless structures have some real function. In the
future we may find that many more of them have some added

[2]E. Kroeber, W. H. Wolff, and R. L. Weaver, *Biology*, p. 483.
[3]W. H. Gregory and E. H. Goldman, *Biological Science*, p. 708.

function, so we should be careful at this point about calling anything useless.

It should be realized too that the extent of usefulness is not the point in question. We know that parts of the body differ as to the importance of their function. It does not seem to be logical reasoning on the part of the BSCS Yellow Version to call the appendix vestigial because "it has been removed from thousands of persons without ill effect."[4] An arm or a leg may be amputated without great harm to the body, but this is no reason to call it vestigial!

It is true that the appendix often does cause considerable trouble. However, this merely puts it in the class with other parts of the body that are often subject to infection. There are probably more cases of sore throat each year than of appendicitis, but no one would go so far as to say that the throat is vestigial and that we would be better off without it.

Scientists do not agree as to the extent of usefulness of the appendix; some think it adds lubricating fluids to the contents of the intestines, others think that it may have an endocrine function; others say it secretes small amounts of digestive juices, and still others think it may manufacture some blood cells and functions in protecting the body from disease. It is possible that it may have some combination of these functions but we are quite sure that it is not vestigial in the true sense of the word.

Next look at some of the ear and scalp muscles that are often classified as being useless. True, they are not as well developed as those in a horse, but they do not need to be. A horse will use them to twitch off a fly, whereas we have other ways of ridding ourselves of these pests! In the human body they may give some protection to underlying parts, attach the scalp to the skull, carry extra blood supply to the ears, and act as "filling material."

[4]Biological Sciences Curriculum Study, *Biological Science: An Inquiry into Life*, Yellow Version, p. 607.

Two lines of reasoning are sometimes presented with the statement that the human embryo has a tail. These are both included by Kimball when he says:

> The fused vertebrae which make up the base of the human spine are interpreted as the vestigial remnants of the tail possessed by our ancestors. In fact, human babies occasionally are born with short tails. These are, however, quickly and easily removed.[5]

Few people would say, as does this author, that the coccyx or end of the backbone is useless. Some very useful muscles are attached to it. We would not entirely discount the other argument which states that sometimes a human baby is born with a short projection that looks like a tail. Evidence indicates that this may have taken place. Could not this be the result of a deranged process taking place during embryonic development? The normal process is sometimes altered and as a result we see Siamese twins, cleft palates and harelips. No one would argue that these were once normal conditions in a remote ancestor. A "tail" could be such an anomaly.

On the inside corner of the eye is a little fold of tissue which is said to be a remnant of a third eyelid. Some reptiles have a third eyelid so this small fold is used to link us to a reptile ancestry. We also note that this tissue is not entirely useless, for it helps to regulate and guide the flow of tears; then, too, *some* tissue is needed there to fill in that corner of the eye!

Next consider the so-called vestigial organs that are spur-like structures on some snakes. Pythons and others have these in the regions where legs are found on other animals. The evolutionist says that this indicates that the snake once had ancestors possessing legs, but there are other possibilities. Even men have lost their legs through changes in the genes within the nucleus of the cells. In L. H. Snyder's *Principles*

[5]J. W. Kimball, *Biology*, p. 545.

of Heredity is a picture of a whole family without legs.[6] This condition is caused by a mutation or change that suddenly appears in the sex cells and is passed on from one generation to another by the usual processes of heredity.

Another thing that might be said about these spurs is that, as with some of the other so-called vestiges, they are not entirely useless. Even though they are covered with skin, some say that they can strike a blow that is useful in combat against an enemy. It may be that they also help to secure traction during locomotion.

The so-called "hip bones" of a whale may also have a very minor function—that of support for some internal organs and places for the attachment of muscles. It is true that cartilage-like bones are embedded in the flesh at about the place hind legs would be if a whale had legs. They are not connected with the backbone and they do not come through to the surface. The whale is a mammal that possesses hair; it also has milk glands with which to feed its young. Since it is a mammal, it is reasonable to believe that God could have created it on the same general plan that He used for other mammals. Of course it had to be modified in various ways to fit it for a life in the water instead of on land. In the same way the bat, another mammal, was modified to fly and was given wings instead of legs. Could not these things show us how conservative God was in His creative patterns?

It also must be recognized that some of these organs which have an obscure and minor use may have degenerated from a more useful condition. When God finished creating various things He saw that they were good, but the entrance of sin into the world has caused many changes which have usually been toward degeneration rather than improvement. Before sin had time to greatly affect the human body, man lived to be hundreds of years old. Gradually his life was shortened, which may have been due to the degenerating influence of

[6]L. H. Snyder, *Principles of Heredity*, p. 401.

sin. It is very possible that some of our organs presently have very different degrees of usefulness from those of Adam, Enoch and Noah. Certainly there are some reasons for a shortened life-span and part of those reasons may be degeneration in some of the organs of the body.

Thinking over this whole section, note that several possible answers to the problem have been suggested. There may have been some degeneration; some parts may have a still undiscovered use; some parts have minor uses; the reduced function of some parts may be the result of a mutation or an injury to the embryo; or it may be that God created a number of animals by using the same general plan.

We may not be sure as to which single thing or combination of things is the correct answer, but we can be sure that any one of them is as logical as what the evolutionist proposes. Every problem has a solution that is in perfect harmony with the Word of God.

11

Origin of Matter and the Universe

An Evolutionary Interpretation

The theory of evolution offers no satisfactory explanation for the origin of matter and of our universe. A person who does not believe in creation by an omnipotent God usually believes that matter is eternal and by itself has produced the changes that have brought about our present universe. This is often called materialism. The dictionary defines this as "any theory which considers the facts of the universe to be sufficiently explained by the existence and nature of matter." Because some of our books use this term interchangeably with naturalism, we will do the same. Naturalism is defined as "the doctrine denying that anything in reality has a supernatural significance."

True organic evolution is usually spoken of as being materialistic and naturalistic because it would rule out God and the supernatural. Few high school texts say that God and miracles either do or do not exist; the subject usually is not mentioned. Typical of these books is the BSCS Green Version's explanation of matter and energy which says, "Living things get their energy from the sun. But they get their matter (substance) from the earth. Organisms are made from the same materials that make up the rest of the world."[1] The book then proceeds to discuss various elements and compounds with no other word than this about what their source might have been. Another book says, "There is no real

[1]Biological Science Curriculum Study, *High School Biology: BSCS Green Version*, p. 11.

89

knowledge of how the sun and its planets came into existence."[2]

CREATIONIST INTERPRETATION

Do these quotations give you some idea of the way high school books give no explanation of the origin of the sun, the earth and other planets? Many scientists say that they are not concerned with origins; for them it is sufficient to take things as they are now and proceed from there. That is what most biology books do.

To have a consistent scheme of thinking about the nature of the universe, it seems necessary to include some philosophy about origins. Admittedly, Christians approach this subject with a preconceived idea. Miracles are tied in with the whole framework of their faith. If miracles are removed from the Bible, there is left only a shell which is worse than useless. It is not logical for a Christian to exclude miracles from his thinking even though he will never be able to comprehend much about the original creation. When asked about how the universe came into existence Christians say, "Faith enables us to perceive that the universe was created at the bidding of God—so that we know that what we see was not made out of visible things" (Heb. 11:3, Twentieth Century N.T.).

Faith is the basic requirement for understanding the universe, all the material from which it is made and all that it contains. To summarize, Christians accept by faith the Bible record which teaches that for His glory and according to His own sovereign will the triune God created; He created all things both visible and invisible; He created all things without the use of preexisting material.

This doctrine of creation is found in almost a hundred passages throughout the Old and New Testaments. Some years ago Christians were laughed at for believing that all

[2]B. B. Vance and D. F. Miller, *Biology for You*, p. 525.

matter in the universe could be made out of "nothing." A creationist had to say, I don't know how it was done; but it is in the Bible so I take it by faith and believe it. As Christians have done this through the ages, their faith often has been turned into sight as new data have been discovered from nature.

Consider what happened early in this twentieth century concerning our knowledge of the structure of matter. As our great-grandparents looked at water, they probably would have said, That is just a drop of water. As scientists studied it they came to realize that a drop was made up of individual molecules. After more study they learned that each molecule was composed of two atoms of hydrogen and one atom of oxygen—atoms so small that billions of billions of them are in a single drop of water. In spite of this minute size it has been possible to study them so that something is known about the electrons, protons and neutrons of which they are made.

Such studies as these involving the structure of matter, have many practical and interesting applications. If one says that the Bible should not be studied because it does not tell all about atomic structure, it is just as unreasonable to not study other scientific areas because the Bible does not tell all one wants to know about them. The Bible gives certain basic facts, and science strives to fill in the details.

More details about the nature of electrons and protons that make up atoms include the fact that it is now realized that they have electric charges which are negative and positive, respectively. The Christian is not surprised to hear that energy and power have always been tied up in matter, for God made the earth by His power (see Jer. 51:15). While energy and power have always been in matter, it has been only recently that man has learned to release tremendous amounts of it by atomic fission.

Outside the Christian viewpoint that God miraculously brought into existence the complicated material of which our universe is composed, there is no logical way of accounting for its origin. The reasonable solution is to believe the Word as it stands. If he wants to, there is no reason why man should not study and speculate further as to just how God brought together the units of structure that make up matter.

As man continues studying the atom, much of his knowledge is gained from work with nuclear reactors and particle accelerators. Because of the way atoms and their parts behave, many scientists have come to believe that all ordinary matter had to be formed in a short time—some say half an hour. It is neither unscientific nor unbiblical to believe that all elements, from which God later formed all things, came into being quickly. The Bible says nothing about the time element needed; it simply says, "God created."

Actually the time element makes very little difference because God does not count time as man does. God, of course, has the ability to do anything in one second or in a billion years. We should not look at one of these time periods as being more miraculous than another. If one considers that the shorter the time (as man counts time) it took for an event to occur, the more power is shown on God's part, he would have to begin to subdivide a second! The smallest part of a second may be an important period of time in many areas of our life today. An athlete may win or lose a race by a thousandth of a second. To send an impulse over eight inches of wire in a computer takes one nanosecond, or one-billionth of a second. Some people say that each act of creation had to take place "instantly." To some this means a minute, to others a second and to others only a fraction of a second. An act is surely no less a miracle if it takes place in any one of these periods of time or even longer ones.

It seems unwise to insist, when there is no objective evidence for it, that God's acts had to be "instantaneous" as we count time. Unless specifically stated, the time element in all the creation story is usually not important. Our measuring of time is not the same as God's. He says through Peter: "Beloved, be not ignorant of this one thing, that one day is with the Lord as a thousand years, and a thousand years as one day" (II Peter 3:8). Don't *you* be ignorant of this! The statement "God created" is the one about which we can be dogmatic.

We realize that we live in a changing world and that science is not static. Today's theories may have to be changed tomorrow as new observations are made and experiments carried out. The two-way communication instrument of Dick Tracy and the space travels of Buck Rogers in one decade seemed improbable and fictitious but in a later one they appear entirely possible.

For many years man has been able to change matter into energy and energy into matter. However, the fact that they are interchangeable does not help the unbeliever explain the origin of either. The inability to do this is one of the weaknesses of the theory of evolution. Before matter and the universe originated, some eternally existing source of power had to exist. The Christian recognizes this when he says, "God has made the earth by His power, He has established the world by His wisdom, and by His understanding and skill has stretched out the heavens" (Jer. 10:12, Amplified).

12

Origin of Life

PROBABLY YOU HAVE OFTEN THOUGHT about some puzzling questions. What is life? How did it begin? What details are connected with the Genesis phrases "God made the beasts of the earth" and "God created man"? Realists down through the ages have asked these same questions. Think how this subject concerns evolution. About half the books being examined do not mention anything about the origin of life and the others tell something of recent experiments in connection with attempts to produce living material in the laboratory. Other authors, like Dodge, mention the subject in such general terms that it is really meaningless: "Through a method not known or understood some giant molecules became possessed with the power to produce others like themselves. Life in its simplest form began."[1]

People who ignore the subject probably say, The origin does not concern us, we merely take the beginning by faith and then go on from there to account for the way life has developed. Evolution has nothing to do with origins; we leave that to the philosopher. We study only development. However, if a person's theory of development is to be reasonable, it will not preclude a reasonable explanation concerning the *beginning* of that development. To avoid the subjects of the origin of life or the origin of matter is to avoid the view that there is a God who is able to perform miracles and who is the ultimate Originator of all things.

The mechanistic view of the origin of life is expressed by one author who says:

[1]R. A. Dodge, *Elements of Biology*, p. 563.

Living creatures on earth are a direct product of the earth. There is every reason to believe that living things owe their origin entirely to certain physical and chemical properties of the ancient earth. Nothing supernatural appeared to be involved.[2]

In another place this same author does say that the question concerning God is outside the realm of science. However, this is still a good example of the way a high school book can eliminate the question of special creation. Not to believe in a Creator is to demonstrate anew the condition of the natural mind that is darkened to spiritual things so that it cannot understand them.

In all our books that do mention the origin of life the following four possibilities are suggested: (1) special creation, (2) life has always existed on the earth, (3) life came here from another planet, or (4) life originated from nonliving material.

The quotation above shows how the first of these, special creation, is given very little consideration. Another author does not believe in creation because he does not believe the truth of the Word of God. In part he says, "Among the first attempts at answering this question in our civilization were the stories of creation that are found in the Bible. Other cultures, too, have their stories of the creation of life."[3] Do you see how he places the Bible on the same level with the stories of other cultures? He then goes on to cast aspersions at the truth of any of these stories because "they invoke divine intervention."

The second of these ideas about life is that it has always existed. This is listed largely for its historical interest but is dismissed by the believer and unbeliever alike as being impossible.

The third way, that life came here from another planet, is seriously considered in some books. According to this hy-

[2]P. B. Weisz, *The Science of Biology*, p. 563.
[3]J. W. Kimball, *Biology*, p. 577.

pothesis it is assumed that resistant spores could withstand the rigors of outer space. In traveling here from a distant planet an organism would encounter tremendous extremes of heat and cold, and deadly radiation. These would be more than life, as known today, could tolerate. Then too, even if life could arrive here from another planet, it would not help to account for the actual beginning of life elsewhere! It would just push our problem back one step farther and so, even as an hypothesis, is of no real help in solving any problem about how life began.

The fourth idea involves spontaneous generation. This means the origin of life from nonliving things. In many books you will find the historical account of this process, which was commonly believed until the seventeenth century, to be interesting reading. Only then did the famous Italian scientist Redi exclude flies from meat to show that under these circumstances maggots were not formed. People used to think that meat produced living "worms" as it decayed. They had not realized that flies laid eggs on the meat and that these eggs hatched into maggots.

In the middle of the nineteenth century Louis Pasteur performed some classic experiments along this same line. In describing Pasteur's work, one book uses the heading "A Challenge to Spontaneous Generation." Pasteur performed many experiments to show that the air was a common source of microorganisms. He held that nonliving material was easily contaminated by living matter because bacteria are always on a person's hands, the soil, glassware and in the air. He demonstrated repeatedly and under a variety of conditions that food and other materials would not produce living organisms after they had been sterilized properly.

In the Pasteur Institute in Paris are two flasks which Pasteur sterilized and sealed before his death in 1895. Their contents are still unchanged. As a result of his work, it is a commonly accepted principle that "life comes from life." In fact, about spontaneous generation, the seventh edition of *Webster's Collegiate Dictionary* says "from a belief now abandoned." The BSCS Yellow Version says: "After Pasteur, few competent biologists continue to believe that spontaneous generation occurs on the earth today. By the beginning of the twentieth century, perhaps none did."[4]

Do you see how the disproof of spontaneous generation left the scientists in a dilemma? If a person does not choose to believe in a God who can create and who is the Originator of life, and if it is unscientific to believe in spontaneous generation, what then can he believe? The unbeliever is forced to make a choice and so he decides in favor of spontaneous generation! He says, "We know that the world was once without life—that life appeared later. How? We think it was by spontaneous generation!"[5] You rightly ask, How can a scientist possibly believe that which is considered to be unscientific? Kimball says:

> Fortunately, a way out of this dilemma was proposed in 1936 by the Russian biochemist, A. I. Oparin. While conceding that life does not arise spontaneously now, Oparin felt that it might well have arisen spontaneously under the conditions that existed earlier in the history of the earth.[6]

Men like Oparin, Urey, Miller and Fox have done much work and speculation about the origin of life and living material. During the last few years accounts of their work have been included in most high school texts. These works should be given some consideration. The most famous of these experiments was carried out with methane, ammonia, water vapor and hydrogen. These four substances, that were supposed to be present in a "primitive earth," were put into an airtight apparatus. For a week they then were circulated past a high-

---

[4]Biological Science Curriculum Study, *Biological Science: An Inquiry into Life*, Yellow Version, p. 42.
[5]*Ibid.*
[6]Kimball, p. 578.

energy spark. Heat and water vapor were supplied from a container of boiling water connected with this apparatus. When at the end of the week an analysis was made of the liquid it was found to contain some compounds that had not been present at the beginning of the experiment. Some complex molecules of amino acids had been formed. These molecules were more complex than the gases from which they were made but were not as complex as protein molecules that make up living protoplasm.

Many scientists think that these and similar experiments show that man has taken a big step toward creating life in the laboratory. This is typical of the way the two ideas are connected:

> The primitive earth probably had an atmosphere of methane, ammonia, water vapor, and hydrogen. . . . It is believed that these relatively simple substances gradually combined into increasingly complex molecules. Finally these complex molecules associated to form systems that had a unique feature: they were self-producing. That is, they could make from the chemical substances around them other systems like themselves. Life had started.[7]

Do you realize what a big gap is jumped between the last two sentences of the preceding quotation? To say "life had started" is pure speculation and wishful thinking. Another author would not draw such a sharp line between the living and the nonliving. In speaking of these same experiments he says that on a "primitive earth" the energy to carry out these reactions would be supplied by the heat of the earth and from lightning. As larger and larger molecules were produced they might form a simple kind of living thing.

> Thus we can imagine a transition rather than a sharp line between complicated non-living things and simple living organisms. . . . Do Oparin's ideas deny Pasteur's conclusions? Not at all. Pasteur was concerned with

[7]BSCS, Yellow Version, p. 635.

conditions on the earth today. Oparin's speculations involved an earth on which very different conditions existed: the atmosphere was different; the temperature was different.[8]

The arguments against spontaneous generation are still valid, but they are valid only for the conditions of today. . . . One most profound difference, of course, was the absence of hordes of hungry living things, seeking every bit of available nourishment.[9]

The question is sometimes asked, if life began in this way [spontaneous generation], is it possible that such primitive forms of life are arising today in the same manner? The answer is no.[10]

Is not this a strange argument to say that spontaneous generation probably happened only once in the distant past but is not now taking place? The best scientific minds of today, working with the best laboratory equipment available, should be able to reproduce "the temperature and atmosphere which existed on the primitive earth." In the laboratory too it is possible to have experimental apparatus free from other living things so that if a living cell was produced it would not be devoured.

One could write a book as thick as a dictionary about the cell and still not include nearly all the facts known about cell structure and function. We realize that some cells are more complicated than others, but to give you an idea of how complex one can be, consider a little of what high schoolers are expected to know about its composition.

Within each cell of your body is a nucleus. Within each nucleus are chromosomes. Within the chromosomes are genes, and we now think that each gene is made up of one (or part of one) molecule. This is a deoxyribonucleic acid, commonly called DNA. Each such molecule is pictured as a

[8]BSCS, *High School Biology: BSCS Green Version*, p. 299.
[9]BSCS, Yellow Version, p. 634.
[10]R. F. Trump and D. L. Fagle, *Design for Life*, p. 46.

double helix by the scientists Watson and Crick. This ladder-like spiral is made up of alternating deoxyribose and phosphate portions of nucleotides. These are linked across from one side of the spiral to the other, like rungs on a ladder or treads on a staircase, by purines and pyrimidines, of which there are four kinds (adenine, thymine, guanine and cytosine). Because the helix is often so long and the various parts we have listed can be combined in different sequences, the number of kinds of DNA molecules is almost unlimited. Someone has said that the possible kinds of combination within one long DNA molecule are as many as are the number of atoms in our earth. Much direct evidence has been learned about DNA by laboratory studies of simple substances such as bacteria, virus and mold. "The conclusion that genetic information is transferred from one generation to the next by DNA is now generally accepted."[11] They also control cell activity and development. At the time of cell division they are capable of duplicating themselves so that each of the billions of cells in our body has exactly the same kind of DNA molecules.

Does this give a small idea of the fantastically complicated molecules within a cell? And yet the evolutionist would have us believe that an original cell happened to come into existence by the *chance* coming together of certain elements. Several authors use this word "chance" and one speaks of the "chance" production of the first living protoplasm. "Even the most unlikely event will probably occur sometime." Most of us would not want to go so far as to say that almost anything can happen once! All evolutionists would not say this, but most of them have a nonmiraculous starting point for their theory.

This question will arise in the minds of some: If life is ever produced in a laboratory, will that be considered evidence for evolution? Some say that it would rather show that a

[11]C. A. Villee, *Biology*, p. 531.

very superior mind is needed to make living material. It is something that could not have happened by the law of chance.

In summary, think over this section concerning the origin of life. It is a problem that evolution does not help solve. The theory of evolution deals with development but offers no explanation for the origin of life. The two speculations, that life always existed on the earth or that it came here from some other planet, are not worthy of real consideration. Spontaneous generation is considered to be unscientific. However, since no other possibility exists, this has to be accepted by those who reject special creation.

Laboratory work of the last few decades, combining simple molecules into more complex ones, is considered by some scientists as lending support to the idea that spontaneous generation may once have taken place. These experiments give us some information about the nature of living material, and possibly something about the methods God used in creation, but they have not solved the problem of origins. Considering the tremendous complexity of even a molecule of a cell, it seems impossible to suppose that this could have happened by chance. We do not agree that "anything could happen once."

It is both biblical and reasonable to take by faith the fact that God is the Author of physical as well as spiritual life.

13

Chance or Design?

THERE IS AN ESSENTIAL DIFFERENCE between the things created by God and the things that are made by man. It is evident to the student that design runs like a thread through all the sciences. No matter which one of them he looks at, he sees design according to a definite plan. He finds it in physics and in biology; he sees order and planning in astronomy and chemistry. The organization within a molecule shows a precision that cannot be duplicated by man. The more the things of nature are magnified, the more evident is the design.

This certainly cannot be said of the things that are made by man. If one would enlarge one of the printed letters on this page, he would see a multitude of imperfections, whereas if a cell or a snowflake were magnified, it would look even more perfect than it did to the unaided eye. Such order and perfection as are seen in the surrounding universe could not have come into existence by themselves. Behind it all there must have been a mind, and it had to be a mind greater than that of man.

As one looks at the human body he realizes the truth of the psalm that says our bodies are "intricately" made (see Ps. 139:15, New Scofield). Even though the body shows corruption as a result of sin, it still has a marvelous complexity that demands an intelligent Maker. The Bible clearly says that God created it: "So God created man in his own image" (Gen. 1:27).

When the body as a whole is considered, one realizes that it could not have come into existence by the ordinary work-

102

ing of the laws of science which are seen around us every day. If only a part of the body, such as the nervous system, is examined, order and planning are still found. One's wonder greatly increases when he examines only a small organ of that system.

Think of the amazing complexity of the eye with its automatically focusing wide-angle lens which takes an instantaneous full-color picture! A doctor may study this organ for years and still feel that he has just begun to know something of its structure and function.

A whole book could be written about the perfection and diversity of the cells from which the eye is made. Even within the elements that make up those cells we see the planning of an intelligent Mastermind.

This atomic age is filled with new knowledge about the smallest subdivisions of these elements. Thus we see marvelous design in the whole nervous system, in just an organ like the eye, or in its cells—or even in the elements and compounds of which they are composed.

George Gallup, originator of the famous opinion polls, says that he can prove God statistically: "Take the human body alone—the chance that all the functions of the individual could just happen, is a statistical monstrosity."

From the perfection seen in the things that are infinitesimally small, we have to stretch our imagination even to begin to comprehend divine planning as seen in the large bodies in space. Our earth, moon, sun, planets and all the stars we can see are just some of the billions of bodies in the Milky Way galaxy. This galaxy in which we live is only one of the billions that exist out in the vastness of space, the closest one being about a million light-years away.

In space, distance is not measured as it is here on the earth, as that would be like measuring the earth's circumference in inches. Instead of using miles, light-years are used. Light travels 186,000 miles a second. Just think of traveling in one

second about eight times around the earth! To find a light-
year, multiply 186,000 by the number of seconds in a minute,
then by the minutes in an hour, then by the number of
hours in a day, days in a week and weeks in a year.. You
would finally arrive at the distance light could travel in a
year and that number would be about six trillion miles. When
we say that our own Milky Way galaxy at its widest point
is about 100,000 light-years from one side to the other, we
really can comprehend neither the number nor the distance.

Can your mind take in the size of the giant stars? Even
our sun is large enough so that if it were hollow, we could
drop a million earths into it. The star Antares is so large that
if it, instead of the sun, were placed at the center of our
solar system it would extend out in all directions as far as
the earth and 100 million miles beyond!

No matter what the size of the object, very large or very
small, we know that it is the truth when we sing "This Is My
Father's World." He is its Designer. To believe otherwise.
seems to be folly to us. It would be like standing in a museum filled with the most beautiful works of art, admiring
them and yet refusing to acknowledge the genius of those
who formed them.

In connection with design in nature, it is conceded that
the argument cannot properly be used to establish the validity of a purely scientific experiment. However, a Christian
scientist, working within a biblical framework, cannot escape
the fact that it exists and therefore it has to color his thinking. The mechanistic point of view is shown in the following
quotations:

> No pattern, no goal can be seen here. No, it is a story
> of adaptations, evolving to meet some immediate need,
> which by chance alone turn out to open new opportuni-
> ties, new, less crowded ways of life to their owners.[1]

[1] J. W. Kimball, *Biology*, p. 615.

We consequently conclude that specific organisms are
not the result of any planned, goal-directed, or pre-de-
termined course of creation.[2]

In the light of what we have presented, does it seem logical
to say that all has happened by chance and that there has
been no planning? We hold that this is not logical and does
not agree with God's revelation in the Bible. He has said,
"The heavens declare the glory of God, and the firmament
shows and proclaims His handiwork" (Ps. 19:1, Amplified).
The argument for creation, because it shows design, is well
expressed by Pearl Kessler in her poem "The Omnipotent
God":

> God of the dawn, and God of the night,
> God of the dark, and God of the light;
>
> God of the flowers, and God of the birds,
> God of the flocks, and God of the herds;
>
> God of the stars, and God of the sand,
> God of the trees, and God of the land;
>
> God of the ages, and God of man—
> This, my God, is a God with a plan.

[2]P. B. Weisz, *The Science of Biology*, p. 715.

14

Man Since Adam

AN EVOLUTIONARY INTERPRETATION

IN CONSIDERING BRIEFLY the subject of ancient man, the teaching of high school texts is examined first. Most clearly state that they believe modern man is the result of organic, materialistic evolution, and all things developed nonmiraculously from a single cell. With increasing complexity and variety, this involved change from one group to another. Therefore, all living things in the world, including man, are related one to the other. Consider a few quotations from our texts which convey this idea:

That modern man has evolved through the operation of the same forces which produced all other organisms is clear.[1]

If we trace back the ancestry of both man and nonhuman primates far enough, we find species that appear to be common ancestors.[2]

The orangutans and chimpanzees and prehensile-tailed monkeys, for example, have specialized in their own ways from more generalized ancestors. In the same way man apparently evolved from his own primate forebears.[3]

Most modern insect-eating mammals, particularly the moles and the hedgehogs, are clearly distinct from modern primates, of which man is a late member . . . insectivorous mammals and primates are very closely related, through a common shrew-like, aboreal insect-eating an-

[1]P. B. Weisz, *The Science of Biology*, p. 753.
[2]R. F. Trump and D. E. Fagle, *Design for Life*, p. 609.
[3]*Ibid.*

cestor. . . . The first distinct primates evolved from this insect-eating ancestor.[4]

Biologists are convinced that the human species has evolved from nonhuman forms of life, and that the human species has reached its present stage of development in much the same way that other species have evolved.[5]

Much time was spent searching for this "missing link," an animal midway between the modern ape and man. From what we know today, the search for a "missing link" was doomed to failure from the start. A missing link between man and some present-day ape does not exist and never did. The relationship between man and the modern ape is like that of distant cousins. Both have had a common ancestor several million years ago.[6]

Some people believe that evolution teaches that man has descended from a monkey or some kind of an ape. The above quotations show that the usual teaching is that both had a common ancestor. Moreover, some of the high school textbooks being considered give the impression that there was a linear amoeba-to-man progression. The term "missing link" is now seldom used, which is indicated in the last quotation. The following quotation holds special interest because it contains this term:

> Proconsul is thought to be 30,000,000 years old. The importance of Proconsul is that he may be the trunk ancestor from which the two branches, ape and human, emerge. . . . Although he could swing in the trees, his arms were not well adapted for that purpose. Although he ran on all fours, it is believed he often walked partially erect. . . . Was Proconsul the ancestor of both man and ape, the "missing link" for which biologists have been searching?[7]

[4]Weisz, p. 472.
[5]BSCS, *Biological Science: Molecules to Man*, Blue Version, pp. 411-12.
[6]W. H. Gregory and E. H. Goldman, *Biological Science*, p. 475.
[7]*Ibid.*, p. 476.

Creationist Interpretation

The biblical record of the creation of man differs from the evolutionary viewpoint that man has evolved from a one-celled organism. It is an account that is sublime and majestic in its simplicity, the climax of the creation story. Because this is such an interesting and important area, look at it closely, considering the Genesis account first.

In chapter 1 of Genesis something is told of the nature of God. He took counsel with Himself and said, "Let *us* make man in *our* image" (Gen. 1:26). Genesis then says, "God created man in his own image, in the image of God created he him; male and female created he them" (1:27). This is all we would have needed to know about the creation of man, but God chose to tell us more. The complementary account of chapter 2 follows as a sequel and is told in colorful language: "And the Lord God formed man of the dust of the ground, and breathed into his nostrils the breath of life; and man became a living soul" (2:7). The English translation of the Genesis account of creation is written in prose and it is interesting to compare it with this poetical account in Psalm 104:3: "[It is God] who layeth the beams of his chambers in the waters: who maketh the clouds his chariot: who walketh upon the wings of the wind." Although this is an inspired verse, it is not necessary to interpret it to mean that the wind has actual wings or that God rides in actual chariots made out of clouds. Similarly, it is not necessary to interpret the Genesis account so literally as to be anthropomorphic. This would mean attributing to God human characteristics such as hands with which to mold dust or nostrils through which to breathe air. It is Job who says, "Thou hast made me as the clay" (Job 10:9). It is in error to interpret either too literally or too figuratively, for one is as bad as the other.

However, one should not say of the creation story, I do not try to interpret it, I take it just as it stands. It is not possible to do this anymore than it is with many other parts of the Bible. One must interpret the parables and analogies, the symbolic and figurative language, the hyperboles and metaphors, the types and antitypes.

For example, the use of the word "leaven" in the New Testament cannot be taken "just as it stands." By many it is interpreted to mean that which is good, whereas others think that it stands for that which is bad or evil. Some think that the "prodigal son" represents a man who has *never* been born-again; others think that he stands for a man who has committed his life to Christ but has become wayward.

Do not be confused into thinking that how one interprets Scripture is a test of whether he believes the Bible to be inspired. He may believe the complete Scriptures are entirely inspired and yet interpret one of the above words in a different manner. We may think that he is being nonbiblical, but surely not non-Christian.

Even though different interpretations of Genesis have been made, our faith that the book is inspired is not shaken. Neither is our faith shaken when someone says we are unscriptural if we do not believe in his favorite interpretation. Scripture is inspired but our interpretations about the "how" of creation are just theories and for that reason little is said in this book about them, although a short account is given in chapter 15.

The phrase "the LORD God formed man" has captured the interest of many scientists. There has been much experimentation and speculation in trying to understand this phrase. Although there is little value for the average man to take the time and energy to experiment and study in this field, there is no reason why he should not do so if he wishes. Such interest and study does not mean that he is leaning toward an evolutionary position.

Some scientists think that the phrase "dust of the earth" means that God made man from the same elements that He put not only into dust but into all of the earthly things that

He created. This would be carbon, hydrogen, nitrogen, oxygen and some of the many other simple substances. Some think that the word "dust" is used here merely to represent very small particles, perhaps even molecules and atoms. In forming man, God could have used fat, protein and carbohydrates that He had previously created. He could have used these to make the muscles, blood and bone of Adam's physical body. *If* God did this, we believe that it was entirely a miracle and was in no way the result of any natural process by itself.

With the biblical account of the creation of man as a starting point, think about some of the questions that have probably come to mind. How long ago were Adam and Eve created? Did manlike creatures live before the time of Adam? Did cavemen really exist? Are the pictures of hairy, apelike creatures in school textbooks real or reconstructions? How does one explain fossils of men that are different from those of men living today? How different are they? Can these differences be explained in such a way as to support the theory of evolution or can they be explained in some other way?

Some of these questions involve areas which the Bible does not touch. God's revelation in the created world has to be studied in order to secure information concerning them. As one studies and examines the fossils and artifacts, seeking answers to these questions, he has to set up interpretations and theories. These interpretations have changed in the past; some of them are still shifting. Undoubtedly more will change in the future as new research continues and discoveries are made. Those who are Christians and scientists should be willing to do this as the change involves no conflict with the clearly delineated parts of the Word of God that are not open to various interpretations. This includes such things as the verses in I Corinthians 15:3-4 that say the gospel is "that Christ died for our sins according to the scriptures; and that he was buried, and that he rose again the third day according to the scriptures."

CAVEMEN

There is no reason to doubt the existence of the cavemen; they were real men given this general name, and living thousands of years before Christ. People actually lived in caves and painted pictures on their walls. Some of these pictures, especially those in southern France and in Spain, are very much like the work of modern impressionists.

One especially interesting Cro-Magnon shelter of rock is at Les Enzies, a village in southern France. It continues to serve human needs for it is the location of a hotel with fine meals and hot baths under the exposed rock walls that in ancient times housed families. Beautifully sculptured ivory has been found in some caves. The colored animal paintings in the Altimire, Lascaux and other places have been called magnificent. On cave walls have been found paintings of various animals, including wooly mammoths, bison, horses, reindeer and fish. Along with the fossil bones of the true cavemen and the things necessary for painting and sculpture, a wide variety of tools and weapons, such as blades, harpoons, arrows, scrapers and spears, has been found.

When the average person hears the word "caveman" he usually thinks of a hairy, thick-necked, chinless, stooped animal related only to the theory of evolution. This is unfortunate, for many facts are known about cavemen but the evolutionist uses only the ones that emphasize his theory. Therefore, the creationist often avoids doing anything with these facts, but this is not a scientific attitude for facts must be faced. The author finds little fault with many pictures of cavemen found in today's elementary and high school textbooks. Most are based on actual skeletons although the foundations of some are reconstructions, that is, a skeleton built from a few bones or parts of bones.

A scientist who knows the field can tell much about a body from its parts. He works in much the same way one .would work if given the breastbone of a chicken and told to use it as a basis for constructing an animal. One would not fashion something that looked like a dog or cat. Known evidence would cause him to construct an animal that had two legs and a pair of wings. Using knowledge about man and other animals as a guide, anthropologists work in the same way to reconstruct a whole animal from only a few bones.

In the past, careful and accurate reconstructions have come into disrepute in some cases because too much supposition was built on too little evidence. When it comes to adding the fleshy parts, imagination, of course, has to be used. In order to emphasize his theory, there have been cases of evolutionists being guilty of adding that which would give the animal a bestial expression. One's thinking should not be influenced by this or by the fact that a caveman is pictured with uncut hair, is unshaven, and wears a skin loincloth. If one walked among some aboriginal tribe today, many of these things might be seen, but they would tell little of the real man living beneath the skin.

When it is said that the cavemen were real men, one may well ask, What makes a man a man? This is a most important question because some of the fossils of ancient men, which are in the books being considered, do not measure up to the standards. To set up standards by which one may judge fossils to be human, two separate areas must be considered. One concerns the body with its mind, emotions and will; the other concerns the spirit. Nonhuman creatures, such as apes and dogs, have both a body and soul. They can think, remember, show affection and even solve problems. As the physical body of man was made from the earth, so was theirs (see Gen. 1:24). However, they do not have the divinely given spirit that God put within Adam when He created him "in his own image" and "breathed into his nostrils the breath of life." This godlikeness is the part of man that is able to do subjective thinking, has moral knowledge, purposeful reasoning, plans for a life after death and can communicate with God Himself. Between the creatures who can do these things and the lower animals there is a great gulf that evolution has not been able to bridge. Man is unique. Keeping in mind these areas(the body, soul and spirit), return to the question What makes a man a man? If one were digging in a hillside several hundred feet below the surface and came upon some bones, how could he tell whether they were the bones of a man or only those of one of the lower animals?

THE BODY

First, consider the body alone:

1. Do the bones show that the individual could have stood erect and had bipedal locomotion? If the fossils were human, the hip and leg bones should be such as would allow an upright posture. This can be deduced with fair accuracy by comparison with modern man.

2. If one found a skull, he would want to know if the individual to whom it belonged had the ability to speak and thereby communicate with his neighbors. Some assumptions would have to be used to answer this but certain necessary muscles must be present. Nonhuman skulls lack a bony process on the inside of the lower jaw where man has attached two pairs of tongue muscles used in speaking. Adam had to speak in order to name the animals.

3. An anthropologist makes many body measurements (especially those of the skull) and works with the ratios and proportions of those measurements, comparing one with the other. These are too complicated to discuss here but, generally speaking, in order to be classified as human, these measurements must fall within certain limits.

4. Humans have a certain type of dental structure. From

the teeth alone it is possible to tell much about the animal
from which they come.

Second, consider the spiritual nature of man and his capacity to build a culture containing tangible items:

1. What artifacts are found with the fossils? When such
things as dishes, tools and weapons (which necessitate ab-
stract thought and planning) are found, one thinks of their
designer as having been a human being.

2. Did the creature, whose bones were found, make use of
fire? At the discovery site of some early fossils have been
found charcoal and, even more important, burned bones and
other indications that the individual had been an intelligent
human being who kindled fires, cooked meat and kept himself warm. These things are not true of nonhumans.

3. Are there evidences that the possessor of the bones had
worshiped a being that he considered superior to himself?
With some fossils are found very simple altars and stones
that have been placed in such a way as to indicate that they
had ceremonial significance.

4. With the fossils, are there any kinds of burial practices
that would indicate a belief in life after death? These need
not be as elaborate as those found in the Egyptian tombs.
Even simple tools or food left with bodies may indicate that
those people thought such things would be of some help in
the next world.

Eight things have been mentioned in the list by which to
judge whether fossil remains are human. Other lists will be
different. One by Dr. George Howe will be found in *God
Created*. A list by Villee includes: (1) The human nose has
a prominent bridge and a peculiar elongated tip. (2) The
upper lip has a median furrow and the lips are rolled out
revealing a mucous membrane. (3) There is a jutting chin.
(4) Man's great toe is not opposable, but is in line with the

others. (5) The human foot is adapted for bearing weight by being arched both lengthwise and crosswise. (6) Man is relatively hairless. (7) The legs are longer than the arms. Note that it is very unlikely for all of these to apply to any one fossil, but one or some combination of them will be present. Leaving the list of criteria, now look at some of the "ancient men" listed in our textbooks. College anthropology books discuss others, but our list will be confined to those most commonly given in high school texts.

South Africa Ape-man (Australopithecus)

The Australopithecus is composed of bones that are undoubtedly very old and it is supposed to be the earliest bipedal animal. The bones are usually dated as being in the early Pleistocene. Most of them were found in the 1920's and 1930's by Broom, Dart and others. Many bones and teeth have been found. Australopithecus is usually assigned a date of astronomical size, one and three-quarters million years. Even though Australopithecus had some human characteristics most of our high school texts say that it was likely nonhuman. According to the first two points of the above outline (about being bipedal and having a special dental structure), Australopithecus is considered hominid. This is the category that includes all fossil and modern man, and is definitely not pongid, the category that includes all modern apes.

We have to be at least as inconclusive in our analysis as the high school books which say there is still evidence to be evaluated, we cannot take these remains to be truly human and, as far as being in the human line, this is only a possibility.

East Africa Man (Zinjanthropus)

Other fossil finds that have such extreme age as Australopithecus assigned to them are the remains of Zinjanthropus. These are discussed in most of the high school books being examined, and we are left with the same conclusion as with

Australopithecus. The first fossils were found by Dr. and
Mrs. Leaky in 1959 at a depth of three hundred feet in the
now-famous Olduvian Gorge in Tanzania, East Africa. The
first skull found looks like a jigsaw puzzle for it is composed
of about four hundred pieces.

Found around these bones was volcanic ash which was assumed to be about the same age. By measuring the potassium-argon ratio in the ash, an age of about 1,750,000 years
has been assigned to these bones. However, there is doubt
as to the accuracy of this dating method, especially when it
cannot be substantiated by comparison with other methods.
Many conservative scientists doubt that the fossils are those
of a human being. He may have been a nonhuman kind that
became extinct many years ago. Some, who feel that Zinjanthropus was a human, think that he was not in the direct line
of modern man.

Near the site of the fossil finds were stones which had been
flaked and chipped into crude tools, or at least some think
they are tools. Because they are of soft limestone, some think
the flaking is a natural phenomenon. Our authors are very
wary about committing themselves to any certain interpretation about Zinjanthropus and we, with them, would say that
much more study is needed.

Java Man

In the early 1890's in the Dutch East Indies the first bones
of the Java man were found by a scientist named Eugène Dubois. He found a skullcap, a femur and three molar teeth.
Later many other bones and bone fragments were added to
the collection. Dubois dated his finds at half a million years
and many more bones were found later in the same and lower
deposits. Most people agree that the characteristics of the
femur bone show that the Java man walked upright. The
first reconstructed drawings continue to be reproduced in the
textbooks even though today it is said that this is not a good

representation of how he must have looked. His posture would have been more upright. Cultural anthropologists think that he was able to speak. However, no certain cultural remains have been found directly associated with the Java fossils.

There seems to be no doubt that Java bones are very old, but even among Christians there is no agreement as to where they should be placed in the history of the world. Some think that he is so different from modern man that he should not be classified as a true human being in the biblical sense. Others think that he might have been a creature that resembled man somewhat, but was not truly human. However, most anthropologists classify the Java man as being a true human being although different from men living today. As a possible descendant of Adam, he may have belonged to a race that was a side branch and not in the line of modern man. The exact age of the Java man's fossils and many things about his culture await further study.

PEKING MAN

Some fossils have been found in China, the best known of which are those of the Peking man. In the 1920's and 1930's hundreds of bones of at least forty different individuals were found in limestone caves and what would have been rock shelters. Most of these were skulls and teeth, although there were some arms, legs and other bones. The date of the Peking man—that of the middle Pleistocene—and his anatomy are much like those of the Java man. He apparently walked erect but was not as tall as the Java man. His skull was thick and the brain was larger, although not as large as that of modern man. The structure of the inside of the skull would indicate that the part of the brain used in speech was well developed. His forehead sloped and his chin receded.

Since the Java and Peking men are so nearly alike anatomically, presumably the Java man had a culture at least as

elaborate as that of the Peking man. Much more was preserved in the Peking cave than in the volcanic Java deposits.
One of the interesting things about the culture of the Peking
man is the indication that he used fire. With his fossils have
been found charred bones, and the blackened areas on the
cave floor indicate that he enjoyed the use of campfires. Flint-
like implements made in such a manner as to lead one to
think that the user had been right-handed have been found.
Tools have been discovered that would have been used for a
number of different purposes. Hand axes and tools for pierc-
ing flesh have been found. There seems to be a good possibility that the Peking men were cannibals, for long bones
were split and skulls punctured in such a way as to suggest
the eating of marrow and brains, in the manner of later
known primitives.

NEANDERTHAL MAN

One of the best known of the prehistoric men, and the one
usually pictured in school books as being a caveman, is the
Neanderthal. About a hundred skeletons have been found
since the beginning of the mid-ninteenth century. He appears to have been short and stocky but, in spite of early pictures and models that show him as having a stooped posture,
it is now believed that he walked upright. His brain was
slightly larger than that of modern man; however, the bones
were thicker, the forehead flat and the brow heavily ridged.
There is evidence that the Neanderthal had some kind of re-
ligious belief. At one site in Italy, south of Rome, a Neanderthal skull was found surrounded by a ceremonial ring of
stones. Other burial sites contain whole skeletons and include
rings of goat and bear skulls, as well as meat containers and
tools left at the graveside presumably for use of the deceased
in an afterlife.

We have some very good specimens of the tools he probably made. Neanderthal tools are called Mousterian because

many were found in a cave in France called Moustier. With these tools he seems to have been a match for the bears and mammoths that lived at the same time.

Practically all scientists agree that he was a true man. Neanderthal bones have been dated by means of fission tracking, potassium argon, and carbon 14. Many scientists agree that these methods of dating place his age at 100,000 years. Even later "classi" Neanderthal were thought by many scientists to be around 20,000 to 60,000 years. After he had become well established in Europe, the Far East and even in Palestine, he suddenly and mysteriously disappeared. No one knows for sure the cause of this disappearance, but he may have been destroyed or absorbed by the Cro-Magnon.

Neanderthal is one of the early men about whom much is known. This is not a case of having nothing but guesswork and reconstructions with which to work; enough bones have been found and dated by modern methods that at least a minimum date for his age can be set. Later in this chapter it is pointed out how he and other early races of men could fit into a biblical chronology. Realize too that there is not complete harmony among Christian scientists on these points.

CRO-MAGNON MEN

Another type of early *Homo sapiens* deserving special attention is the Cro-Magnon, who is thought to have taken over some of the caves where Neanderthal man once lived. It seems reasonable to accept at face value the account as given in most high school texts. The following is typical:

> Throughout Europe, in France, Italy, Poland and Czechoslovakia the remains of **Cro-Magnon** men have been discovered. Over a hundred fossils helped reconstruct a composite man looking something like the following:
>
> He was about six feet tall. He had a high forehead

and his cranium was about 1600 cubic centimeters in volume. He made fine stone tools as well as delicate implements from bone and ivory. Some historians credit him with the invention of the bow and arrow. He was also an artist of considerable ability.

On the walls of the caves in which the Cro-Magnon remains have been found are the paintings for which he is famous. Using only red earth and black animal charcoal from charred bones, he achieved remarkable results. He painted the animals he hunted—bears, mammoths, horses and bison.[8]

There seems to be sufficient evidence from the dozens of skeletons found for accepting a date of 20,000 years and even older for this intelligent race which in many ways was physically superior to men living today. Such people actually lived and possessed the characteristics usually attributed to them; they are neither imaginary nor are they misinterpretations.

Because their physique and culture were more advanced than those of other men who lived at the same time and later, some people use Cro-Magnon to show that the history of man has not been one of continual upward progress. There have been periods of degeneration. There are those who say that there have been degenerative periods even in man's culture alone. After reaching a high degree of development certain skills of the Egyptians (such as those used in building the Pyramids and Sphinx, making stained glass and embalming mummies) were practically lost for centuries. The same thing is true of other ancient civilizations; we often find a less specialized one replacing one that is more advanced.

Thus culturally as well as physically, as seen in the Cro-Magnon man, the human race has often undergone a change that is not improvement. The materialistic evolutionist recognizes this and reveals it in his writings that are geared to the university level, where it is usually made clear that he

[8]Gregory and Goldman, pp. 481-82.

does not believe in an amoeba-to-man progression up through an apelike missing link to the human beings of today. Unfortunately the idea of a missing link between man and an apelike ancestor is found in many elementary and secondary texts, where the idea is clearly stated that man is becoming more complex and specialized and usually progressing onward and upward.

The evolutionary position, as stated by Vance and Miller, says, "Judging from the amount of change that has taken place in the past, we may reasonably expect that we shall continue to change in the future. . . . We may expect a superrace."[9] Trump says, "He is surely continuing to evolve."[10] And, "as we learn more about ourselves we have the priceless opportunity of becoming more human."[11] We feel that this whole idea is fallacious for no one was more human than Adam when he walked and talked with God in the Garden of Eden.

FONTECHEVADE FOSSILS

Fontéchevade fossils illustrate another interesting point. If ape-to-man evolution were true, as is presented in some texts written for secondary schools, it would seem that the oldest fossils should be the most primitive in structure. However, some of the examples of a primitive type are not chronologically the oldest. The anthropologist recognizes the fact that if we arrange our fossils of men according to their age, their shape and structure do not fit in with a unilinear theory of evolution. The evolutionist does not always see this. For if, in turn, we arrange their shape and structure to fit the theory, they are no longer arranged from the youngest to the oldest. In France, the Fontéchevade fossils were found in a cave under stalagmite layers above which some more primitive type Neanderthal fossils were found. This is an exam-

[9]B. B. Vance and D. F. Miller, *Biology for You*, p. 539.
[10]Trump and Fagle, p. 617.
[11]*Ibid.*, p. 621.

ple of the more primitive fossils according to their form (the Neanderthal ones) being found in later strata than those (like the Fontéchevade ones) that show more modern characteristics such as no indications of Neanderthal brow ridges.

PILTDOWN MAN

The Piltdown man is of historical interest. Note that real scientific scholars are not intentionally trying to falsify evidence and fool the general public, for most are men who exercise serious intellectual effort. Problems are met, studied, acknowledged and corrected.

In past years Piltdown fossils were some of the most controversial. A lower jaw, some teeth and a number of thick skull bones were found in 1912 in England and were given varying old dates by different geologists and anthropologists. From the beginning these bones puzzled scientists because the skull bones seemed to be human and the jawbones that of an ape. But there were no apes in England and no evidence that there ever had been. As new methods of dating and study were devised, they were applied with special interest to the Piltdown man in an effort to clear up the mystery surrounding him. The "hoax" was widely publicized in 1953 when it was established that the jaw had belonged to a different creature from that of the skull. It was shown that the teeth had been altered by an artificial abrasive, stained with iron alum, and may even have had some black paint added. We may never know who perpetrated this intentional forgery and for what reason, but note that the same scientists who were puzzled by these bones, were the first to admit their error and were glad to have the mystery solved. The Piltdown fossils should also teach us not to be too dogmatic about isolated "finds." Even when we possess the bones, it is possible for misunderstandings about them to arise.

Scientists have to work in this way: they set up theories, study them and then break them down and start all over again. If this had not been true of Edison and Ford, they never would have invented the things that we enjoy today. Paul Ehrlich is a good example of a man who worked this way in trying to find a drug to kill the germ that causes syphilis. With 605 drugs he experienced defeat, but it was during his 606th experiment that he found a compound that would cure most cases of syphilis. Although it is now seldom used since other drugs have replaced it, it saved many lives and is still called "606." Moreover, theories about fossil men cannot easily be tested because these men are no longer alive, thus these theories may be subject to more error than the experiment just mentioned.

Also consider the fact that the chance of any one thing becoming fossilized is extremely small because conditions for fossil formation are very rigid. There is also the possibility of abnormal forms becoming fossilized. When this happens there is a very small proportional chance of such an abnormal fossil being found and studied. The chance that the fossil of an abnormal form should be produced, found and studied is less than the chance of finding a needle in a haystack. Therefore, do not insist that a fossil is likely to be one of some unusual living thing. Occasionally one reads accounts of such things as two-headed calves, Siamese twins, pituitary giants or dwarfs, or skeletal changes caused by dietary deficiency diseases such as rickets, or acromegaly caused by an overactive pituitary gland. If one of these skeletons should be found, it would be possible to conclude that a race of animals far removed from the normal for that particular group had existed at that special time. Recognizing that fossils could be produced of such an abnormal or atypical form, one must also realize that the probability is less than of the more numerous "normal" form.

Recall what has been said about these eight ancient "men." Some books being considered give others, but our list includes those most often mentioned. There is little evidence that the first two, those from South or East Africa, are the remains of humans. A few question the next two, Java and Peking, but most scientists accept them as being fossils of true men. Almost all scientists will agree that Neanderthal, Cro-Magnon and Fontéchevade fossils were the remains of human beings. The Piltdown man was mentioned for its historical interest. If we accept some of these old fossils as being true men and assign to them an age greater than the 4004 B.C. date of Ussher, or even an age a few years older than his, is there a harmony between this greater antiquity of man and the Scripture? Since many people skip over the Old Testament genealogies with only a superficial reading, there are some things they may never have noticed. Ussher's date is based on the assumption that the genealogies are meant to be complete and that the dates given may be added together to give the years lapsing between different events. But the chronologies are not set up to show the exact father-to-son relationship one usually thinks of. Therefore, one cannot add the ages of the patriarchs to arrive at the length of time from them back to Adam. Total dates are given for time between some events in the Bible but none is given for the time between (a) the beginning of creation and the creation of Adam, (b) Adam and the flood, nor (c) the flood and Abraham.

One cannot add the ages given for the patriarchs for several reasons. For example, the word "son" as used in the Bible should sometimes be translated "descendant." This would be a better translation for the word "sons" in Genesis 46:18: "These are the sons of Zilpah, whom Laban gave to Leah his daughter, and these she bare unto Jacob, even sixteen souls." One learns from verses 16 and 17 of this chapter that the sixteen "sons" of Zilpah included two sons, eleven grandsons, one granddaughter and one great-grandson. Therefore, when it says that these sixteen souls were the "sons" of Zilpah it really means that they were her descendants.

Another thing to notice in connection with the use of the word "sons" is the long time gap that may be present. In Matthew 1:1 it says that Jesus Christ is the son of David, the son of Abraham. Instead of this referring to three succeeding generations, only these three names are listed to bridge over nearly two thousand years of Jewish history. Here, as in other places, it seems that only some of the important or outstanding men are named. It has been suggested that some of the names in the genealogy of Genesis 5 are names of men in a whole dynasty. The "son" mentioned might be the name of an important man and the year number might be the beginning of the dynasty.

Listing only a few important people, as in Matthew 1:1, is consistent with the selective style that meets God's purpose and was the custom of the times of the writing of the first two chapters of Genesis. Of the various plants that He created, He lists only grass, herbs and fruit trees. Of the various animals He lists whales, fish and creatures of the sea, fowls of the air, creeping things of the field, beasts and cattle. The whole Bible had to be written in a very selective way, for in John 21:25 we read about the life of Christ: "There are also many other things which Jesus did, the which, if they should be written every one, I suppose that even the world itself could not contain the books that should be written." When it is said that a man "begets" another, it does not always mean that he has born to him a direct son. Eleven names of those "begotten" by Canaan are given in Genesis 10:15-18. Two of these are sons and the other nine are families or nations. Here "begat" means that this man became the ancestor of both sons and nations.

The use of the word "begat" to mean "be designated the ancestor of" can clearly be seen in the story of Abraham. In

Genesis 11:26 we are told that Terah lived 70 years and begat Abram, Nahor and Haran. Other places in the Bible give no indication that these three were triplets, all born when their father was 70 years old, so other Scripture must be examined. In Acts 7:4 it says Abraham left Haran when his father died and, according to Genesis 12:4, Abram was then 75. Genesis 11:32 says that his father died at the age of 205 so Terah must have been 130 when Abram was born.

When Terah died he was .205
This was when Abram left Haran at age 75
By subtracting, we find the age of
Terah at Abram's birth to be 130

If, then, Terah was 130 when Abram was born what is the meaning of Genesis 11:26 which says he was 70? The Bible likely means that when Terah was 70 he was designated the ancestor of Abram who would be born 60 years later. How much later Nahor and Haran were to be born these verses do not tell us.

Another gap in a genealogy record is seen in Ezra 7:1-4, where it says in verse 3 that Azariah is the son of Meraioth. Compare this with I Chronicles 6:7-10 where four other names are inserted between Azariah and Meraioth.

Now look at Matthew 1:8, which says Joram begat Ozias (Azariah). In I Chronicles 3:11-13 the names of Ahaziah, Joash and Amaziah are added between these two men.

What might seem to be discrepancies in the chronology of the genealogical record should not be connected with any lack of inspiration of the Bible. In some cases, ways of speaking and terms used were different in biblical times from what they are now. In other cases it is in keeping with the selective way in which God wrote His Word, with the emphasis on the redemption of man. In no way can these be considered "errors" in the Scripture, which is completely trustworthy and our final authority. Since the rest of the Bible bears out the fact that there were gaps in the genealogical records of Genesis, one may well ask what possible limits of time were involved. Although it is impossible to answer this question, we believe evidence does not allow for astronomical dates that run into millions of years. However, it does allow for ones much older than those proposed in the seventeenth century by Ussher, and arrived at by simply adding together dates given for the different patriarchs.

Evidence pointing to a much older date for Adam than that arrived at by Ussher cannot be ignored and warrants a serious nonevolutionary study. This older date in no way conflicts with the Bible, our final authority; it only conflicts with some men's special interpretation of it.

Since the Bible is not specific about a date for Adam, most scholars are willing to look to science for help in determining man's antiquity. In no way is science being set above the Bible for we know that harmony exists between God's created world and His written Word. It was God who set into operation the various laws that govern radioactive and other dating methods.

Radioactive dates are not laws in themselves; rather, they are ratios set up by man and are based upon certain assumptions. Facts do exist, and Christian scientists are continually searching and studying to try to find them. Maybe you will be such a scientist who will help by filling in some information that, as yet, is incomplete.

In comparing fossils and living men, one has to acknowledge that there has been a good deal of change since Adam. Some of these changes have been great enough to produce races of people quite different from those living today. However, there is no series of fossils leading up to modern man that would connect him with lower primates. Such a series as this, based on anatomy, is shown in the BSCS Green Version,[12] and one can find such a series in many museums.

[12]BSCS, *High School Biology: BCSC Green Version*, p. 660.

Nevertheless, such a series does not exist and, as the legend under the picture in the book just mentioned states, this is an "Artist's reconstruction of heads of some hominids," and naturally it is drawn with the idea of giving support to the theory of evolution.

Not only is evidence lacking for a graded anatomical series connecting man with lower animals, but there is no evidence of his having had a beginning of what we would term human culture even though cultural progress is very evident. Even among the fossils of some of the very old true men are found evidences that they possessed a knowledge of music, the ability to make tools and to create various works of art. This cultural gap between the lower animals and man is just as important as the anatomical gap, and it is one that is significantly vacant.

No matter what evidence about the age of men is felt valid to accept, that age is very, very recent when compared with the earth's history as proposed by uniformitarian geologists. Look again at the time scale in Figure 4. When one realizes that humans did not appear until the Pleistocene, it is obvious that no matter where one places Adam, fossils of his descendants are found only in the upper, more recent years.

Four of the twelve books being considered use the idea of a clock or calendar to represent the earth's history. Kimball uses a twenty-four-hour clock to represent the entire history of life from its beginning to the present, which he pictures as being midnight.[13] He represents life's origin as taking place very early in the twenty-four hours and, as he follows around his clock scale, adds other events at various times. His last two notes are: "Man first appeared at 11:59 P.M." and "Recorded human history begins ¼ second before midnight."

Such a scale is based on the idea that true men are one or two million years old—a concept we do not accept. Many evolutionists also do not use such large dates for the age of

[13]J. W. Kimball, *Biology*, p. 582.

man. One book says, "But our own species, Homo sapiens, does not appear to have arrived earlier than the last glacial stage, about 25,000 to 50,000 years ago."[14]

Many scientists, evolutionists and creationists alike, feel that man's history is very short compared with the age of the earth. In this connection, read chapter 15 where the weaknesses of the various theories are not analyzed, but some of the ways are listed by which various Christian scientists have tried to solve this puzzle. How can there be a seemingly old age for the earth and a comparatively young one for the age of man?

Facts about early men and nonhuman forms, and how to differentiate between the two, have been learned from almost every field of science. There have been contributions from biology, mathematics, chemistry, physics and new sciences such as atomic physics. Many less-known specialized skills, or ones that the ordinary person often does not associate with this type of work, are also used. While excavating in the field, the geologist helps in picking the site and giving information about such things as erosion, volcanic action and mountain building. A surveyor maps the site and records contour data that will be obliterated after digging has been done. The work of a draftsman is important to record the exact horizontal and vertical position of all fossils, tools and artifacts that are found. A photographer makes a constant record of all work as it proceeds. Preparator is the name given to a person who does many things like encasing fragile parts in plaster casts. A paleoanthropologist coordinates the work of all these people as well as of those who work in the laboratory.

After the material is brought into a laboratory the geophysicist and geochemist study not only the composition of the fossils and artifacts that have been unearthed, but they also carry out such dating tests as the carbon 14 and the potas-

[14]Gregory and Goldman, p. 716.

sium argon. A paleontologist studies fossils which tell him what the fossilized plants and animals were like when they were alive. A physical anthropologist works closely with the field geologist to answer questions having to do with identifying and classifying rocks and minerals at the excavation's location. The palynologist specializes in the study of plant pollen. As mentioned elsewhere in this book, the study of pollen helps to show something of the habitat and the diet of living things of a special area at a particular time. His work is closely associated with that of the pedologist, who is a specialist on soils and their composition. A pedologist studies the core bored from the earth and gathers such information as that given earlier about living things and about the soil beneath the Palace of Fine Arts in Mexico City.

Some of the sciences involved in the study of fossils and artifacts have been listed to show that this is a truly scientific field. Results from an honest study in these composite areas cannot be lightly ignored. However, there are some simple facts to which one must always return. The inspired Word and the created world both originated in a God of truth. For this reason, it is only when one of them is misinterpreted that there may seem to be a lack of harmony between the two. It is the goal of the Christian scientist to seek for correct interpretations. Although he knows that harmony exists, he also knows that it often takes real study to discover this harmony.

Therefore, be willing to study. In some areas it would seem wise not to be too dogmatic because there are problems for which the solutions are still being sought. That there are questions does not mean that an answer does not exist. Of one thing, though, we can be certain—some thousands of years ago God miraculously created the first man from whom we have all descended. "For thou hast created all things, and for thy pleasure they are and were created" (Rev. 4:11).

15

Time of Creation

IN DIFFERENT CHRISTIAN GROUPS there are a number of different theories concerning the time when creation might have taken place, how long the process took, and other related subjects. You probably will come into contact with people who believe each of the theories mentioned here, and since you want to be a well-informed person as well as satisfy your own curiosity, you will want to know something about them. These interpretations have been proposed by sincere Christians who believe the Bible. These Christians see a variety of facts in the world of living things and in the now-fossilized organisms that lived during past ages. We are interested in finding a way to explain these scientific facts.

Since it would take a whole book to analyze the various theories about to be mentioned, all we can do is, in a general way, mention what each one presents and not be specific about their various weaknesses. The only one to be presented in detail is the first one because the author feels that it has the most evidence in its favor. However, as with all the others, let us recognize that it is a theory and so is subject to changes, as are all interpretations.

Because the Bible has very little or nothing to say about many subjects, Christians have speculated about what they think might be interpretations for the facts seen in God's created world. Don't forget that these speculations are theories. Of course they all cannot be true, although there is probably some truth in all of them! This chapter should help one to not be tolerant of those who tamper with changes in

any of the clearly defined doctrines of the Bible. Creation by
God is, of course, one of these doctrines and we are tolerant
of various ideas *only* where human interpretation of the details enters the picture. An interesting thing to note is that
various people can look at one Scripture portion very differently. One may say of another's theory, No, that is a very
poor interpretation.

This is evident if one reads several of the books listed in
the Bibliography. These books support the various interpretations set forth in this chapter. No two of these books agree
in *every* detail. All of these authors believe that "in the beginning God created the heaven and the earth," but they differ widely in what they think about the *time* and the method
of creation. These authors are all sincere in their beliefs and
are writing only because they think that their way of inter-
preting the Scripture most closely fits the facts.

Note that even among Christians a great variety of opinions exists and that no good will come from ridiculing one
who differs in some detail from your interpretation. Most
Christians who hold to these various theories are truly searching for the one and only true teaching of the Bible.

BIBLICAL CREATION

The Genesis account of creation is one of the most beautiful passages to be found in all literature. It is simple enough
for even a child to understand the basic facts and yet so
complex that no one comprehends all its meaning. Majestic
is a suitable word often used for this beginning of God's perfect Book. Although there are many translations of the seven
first Hebrew words, most people prefer the Authorized or
King James Version, "In the beginning God created the
heaven and the earth" (Gen. 1:1). No date is given for this
event, but from the best scientific evidence available today,
making use of the dating methods and their assumptions
mentioned in chapter 4, one might infer it took place between

four and five billion years ago. The length of the "days" or
the periods of time is not given.

Obviously each "day" was shorter than the one of Genesis
2:4 which says, ". . . in the day that the LORD God made the
earth and the heavens," for "day" as used in that verse includes all of the other six.

After the grand opening sentence some of the details are
given. For example, Genesis 1:2 states that the earth was
"without form, and void," meaning that it was shapeless,
empty and uninhabited. The illustration is sometimes used
that the formless earth at this early stage of creation was like
a shapeless stone, ready for the sculptor to form it into a
beautiful object. So God fashioned the elements and compounds that He had created into the earth we now know.
Compared with the *fact* that God is the Creator, the *time*
He used for each step in preparing the earth as a place for
man to live is of little significance, but it is interesting to
study.

It is also interesting to study what the earth shows about
the various steps. One thing is that it was once hotter than
now. Evidence indicates that this was during the first days
of creation and before any living thing was created. The
cooling process accounts for some of the rock foldings and
irregular surfaces of our planet. While the earth was hot,
water could not exist on it in a liquid form. Dense banks of
water vapor may have caused it to be dark. The possibility
that the sun was not even created until the fourth day is
mentioned later in this chapter.

As the first day progressed and the earth cooled more and
more, and the clouds of vapor became less dense, God said,
"Let there be light" (1:3). We can only speculate as to the
source of this light; we are not told. There are lights such
as phosphorescence and the aurora borealis that are not connected with the sun. Some think it was a cosmic light; others
that it was from the sun, hidden by clouds until it was made

to appear on the fourth day. It has even been suggested that
this light might in some way be connected with the Shekinah
glory of the Lord of which we so often read in the Old
Testament. On the second day or unit of time, God caused
a space or expanse to appear, dividing the water vapor above
the earth from the water on the earth. The earth may have
continued its cooling process while this took place.

On the third day God caused the dry land to appear and
the water, which evidently had covered the whole earth, to
be gathered together so that this could take place. There
are many indications that this day lasted for a long time with
land rising and falling, and the continents and oceans changing their size and locations. Many think that the areas toward
the North and the South Pole cooled first, so that plants grew
there first. The Bible does not say, but fossils of plants are
found in those regions where it is now too cold for them to
grow. God did say, "Let the earth bring forth . . . [plants]"
(1:11).

The great Potter, after shaping the empty earth, began to
stock it to be ready for His creation of man. Great forests
grew and became coal for man's use. Most of the vegetation
from which it was formed grew in slowly submerging swamp-
lands. The greater the pressure on top of the huge plant
deposits, the higher the grade of the coal. Only God, perhaps
working through the natural processes He had set into operation, could have combined the right amount of pressure,
moisture and temperature to form the bituminous and an-
thracite coal that is used today.

The biblical account of the fourth day gives all the important facts one needs to know, but not all the details in
which one might be interested. God said that there were
to be lights in the firmament of the heaven. These lights
were to divide the day from the night and were to be for
signs and seasons and for days and years. A great light was
to rule the day and a lesser light the night. There were to

be stars and all of those were to give light upon the earth. We take this account by faith but we are also interested in how it can be interpreted. One possibility is that the sun and moon were created before the fourth day but were hidden by vapor and only made to appear at this time. On a cloudy day one cannot tell whether it is morning or evening just by looking at the sky. From a cloudy sky alone, one cannot tell the seasons as is possible when one can see where the sun rises and sets. On this fourth day God may have removed the vapor so that the previously created heavenly bodies could be seen clearly. As has been said, this is just one interpretation or theory.

As God continued to fill and prepare the earth for the creation of man, animals were created. On the fifth day the waters were to bring forth *abundantly* various living creatures. Both large and small animals were then given time to multiply and fill the sea. Some of them were so small that millions could be found in a single pailful of water. He also created the great whales or, as the Revised Version states, "great sea-monsters." The blue whale of today sometimes exceeds one hundred feet in length, and a squid may be fifty feet long.

It seems like an artificial arrangement to try to connect each creative day with a specific period in geological time, and this cannot be done consistently. However, they do harmonize at certain points, although many problems exist. For instance, the creation of fish on the fifth day had to be before the Devonian period. It was during this time, after God had told them to be fruitful and multiply, that they became the dominant form of life. We call the Devonian period the Age of Fishes. God created birds, and geology shows us that during the Jurassic period they were the most abundant.

The beasts and cattle on the sixth biblical day surely must have included mammals. The picture here as well as in

God's created world seems to show that they were the last animal to be created. One cannot be sure, for the term "cattle, and creeping thing and beast" (1:24) is a very broad one. It is known that fossils of the mammals are found first in the Cretaceous and not in earlier strata. Again, the length of time taken for the creation of these animals is not given, but evidently the creation of one followed the other. Neither is it told how many were created. But, whatever the number, they were created "after their kind" and this is valid evidence against the development of "kinds" by evolution.

The creation of man in God's image was the climax of the creative events. Man was given a moral and spiritual nature with mental and esthetic characteristics not found in beasts and cattle. The creation of man was a definite act of God and in no way the result of an evolutionary process. Man's creation as the last of the created living things is seen in both God's Word and in His world. Fossil remains of man are not found, for instance, in the Cambrian rocks where evidence points to the fact that the animals fossilized in these rocks were created long before Adam. Dinosaurs and many other animals now extinct were probably never seen by man.

God rested from His creative work after He had created Adam and Eve. He had brought the universe into existence and in an orderly way had prepared the earth to be a place for men to live. Only after He had prepared that which had been without form and empty at the beginning, and had stocked it with plants and animals, did He create man to have dominion over all these things.

This biblical account of creation combines the two ways God works: (1) supernatural miracles, and (2) His established laws of natural process. He used the same two methods throughout the Old Testament. Usually He carried out His purposes by means of laws such as those of gravity, growth and reproduction. Sometimes He acted apart from these laws and fed people with manna, raised the dead and healed the lepers. When He walked here on earth He also worked in both ways. Often miracles were associated with the initiation of a new major event such as the exodus or the founding of the first church. Therefore Christians do not wonder at the fact that many miracles are connected with the various events of creation.

In this age of grace God still works by directing natural processes as well as by performing miracles. One of His greatest miracles is creating a new creature by means of the new birth.

From "in the beginning" until the creation of man, God performed many miracles to bring into existence things that had not existed previously. He also set into operation many processes with which one comes in contact every day. Even though they have existed since the beginning of time, the details of some of these phenomena, such as those controlling atomic structure and energy, are just beginning to be understood. The longer one lives and studies, the more details he expects to learn. Although these always are interesting, one must realize that some parts of the creation account can never be fully comprehended. "By faith we perceive that the universe was fashioned by the word of God, so that the visible came forth from the invisible" (Heb. 11:3, NEB).

The fact that we cannot know all the details about creation in this life should not keep us from studying it. It is "through faith" that we understand as much as we do about most of the great doctrines of the Bible. There is much about the doctrine of the Trinity that we cannot understand and so have to take by faith, but that should not deter us from studying the subject. We study about the Holy Spirit (in fact, some men devote much of their lives to this one subject) and yet, along with our interpretation of what the Bible says, much is known only by faith. We should study prophecy even though we realize that the most profound scholars of the subject will never arrive at a complete knowledge of all its intricacies.

Using these four illustrations as examples, think about this question: Since I cannot understand all there is to know about creation, the Trinity, the Holy Spirit or prophecy, isn't it just as well for me not to be concerned with studying these subjects but to wait until I get to heaven to learn most of what I want to know? In reality wouldn't this be treating one biblical subject as being less inspired than another? God has given us truth to be studied in order to learn more about Him. Some of this truth is found in His created world. His purpose is not to hide information, but it does not always lie on the surface. We are encouraged to study and dig for it. This is especially true of difficult subjects as those mentioned above. As we study, we can pray for God's help to reveal to us the true meaning of His Word. It is not possible for the Bible to tell all there is to know about any one subject for "the world could not contain the books." However, that which is given is given to be studied. Many mature Christians read the Bible through each year or in some definite period of time. They continue to do this because they realize that "*all* scripture is inspired by God and is useful for teaching the faith and correcting error, for resetting the direction of a man's life and training him in good living" (II Tim. 3:16, Phillips).

The fact that we are living in the age of grace should not limit our study to the New Testament alone. Just as neglecting any single book because it seems difficult or incompletely treated in the Bible is really saying that book is less important or less inspired than some other part, so neglect of any particular subject indicates the same attitude. Rather than neglect the study of creation, do we not have a double reason for devoting some time to it? First, as mentioned previously, God says the created world is one of His revelations to man. In it one learns some things about God's power, glory and handiwork. The second reason for studying this general subject is that it is part of the *"all* Scripture" given by inspiration and therefore profitable for diligent contemplation and examination.

In studying the subject of creation, both in the written Word and as revealed in nature, consider whether what you learn could not be schematically represented in one of the following ways:

A.

| Creative acts of the first twenty-four-hour day. | Long period of time. | Creative acts of the second twenty-four-hour day. | Long period of time. | etc. |

B.

| First long day with various creative acts distributed throughout it. | Second long day with various creative acts distributed throughout it. | etc. |

Since there is no real direct biblical evidence, these obviously are theories. Other scientists would include more than these two, but this author thinks these are the best. Of these two, we would favor diagram B. Some people very strongly favor outline A because it allows acceptance of a twenty-four-hour creative day and also an old age of the earth that nature seems to demand. However, the same Hebrew word that is translated "day" many times in the Bible, refers to a long period of time as it is used in scheme B. Many biblical phrases use the word "day" to refer to a long period of time in the same way in which we say, In the day of Martin Luther, or, Before the day of Thomas Edison. It is understood that we are not referring to a twenty-four-hour day. Many such phrases are in the Bible: "day of salvation," "day of the Lord," "day of anger," "day of Jerusalem," "day of Jesus Christ" and "day of prosperity."

In presenting a case for a twenty-four-hour creative day, some cite the use of the phrase "and the morning and the evening" were of such and such a day. In this connection, it should also be noted that the Bible uses these terms in connection with longer periods of time. In speaking of the grass, Psalm 90:6 says, "In the morning it flourisheth, and groweth up; in the evening it is cut down and withereth." This surely is not referring to a literal morning and evening of a twenty-four-hour day, and the same just might be true in the Genesis account of creation. As mentioned, in Genesis 2:4 "day" is used to refer to all of the creative days. As noted, either diagram A or B can be used without doing violence to the Genesis account of creation as far as our present understanding is concerned. In either case there is room for a lapse of time between creative acts, which seems to be the picture conveyed in both God's Word and His world. On both these bases, it seems that scheme B is better. The Word allows it and in nature are found many rock strata and great periods of time seem to separate fossils of one kind from the sudden appearance of another kind. Just as this sudden appearance of new forms (indicating another act of creation) argues against the theory of evolution, so also does it argue in favor of the creative acts being spread out over a period of time.

Before continuing, let it again be said that this is a matter of interpretation. No two theories can both be correct, for obviously creation happened in only one way. Since born-again men who are both scholars and scientists still disagree on some of the thories concerning creation, we may even wonder if the one true interpretation has yet been found! Anyway, it seems wise not to be dogmatic.

Now let us examine some entirely different theories concerning the time of the events of creation. As mentioned, the theories are simply presented and not analyzed for their weaknesses—which they all have (including that of the author).

THE GAP THEORY

Those who adhere to this theory accept the scientific evidence that points to the earth having a very old age. To account for this, they see in the first sentence of the Bible "In the beginning God created the heaven and the earth," an original creation probably very much like our earth today. While it existed, most of the rock strata and fossils were formed. Dinosaurs and other animals could have flourished and then become extinct. Plants and animals of this era would have become today's petrified forests, coal and oil.

Following this original creation, a great cataclysm is supposed to have destroyed the earth so that it became "without form, and void." This destructive event is usually associated with the fall of Satan and his angels. Genesis 1:2 would then be the beginning of an account of a re-creation during which time God reconstructed the earth, fashioning it into the form seen today.

Although not quite synonomous, a variety of names is given to similar hypotheses and the one used will depend largely upon where a person wishes to place the emphasis. Since it is simple, we have used the term "gap theory." Other names sometimes used are: reconstruction, creation—ruination—re-creation, restitution, interval, cataclysmic, and divine judgment.

Through much of the nineteenth century many held to this theory for they realized that evidence pointed to the necessity for giving to the earth a very old age. At the beginning of the twentieth century the gap theory became even more popular because it was included in the footnotes of the Scofield Reference Bible published in 1909. Editors of the 1967 revised edition have omitted or changed many of the head-

ings and footnotes. The gap theory, instead of being presented in such a positive way, is now given as a mere possibility.

THE TOPICAL ORDER THEORY

The traditional view of the Genesis account of creation is
that the events are listed in chronological order, but some
think that the various events might be given in a topical
order. This is one way to explain such events as the sun
being made to appear clearly on the fourth day whereas
plants had been mentioned as being created on the third.
The topical theory would be much like your father telling
you that he had built a summer cottage. He might say, "I
built it all; the roof, the walls and even the fireplace." It is
understood that you do not think of him as having done the
work in that order. In the same way, it is said that God
could have, in a topical order, listed the creative events of
Genesis. If we were giving a critique of these various theories, we would say that this one has very little evidence to
support it!

CANOPY THEORIES

Another interesting area concerns canopy theories. Theories have been proposed suggesting that the early earth was
once surrounded by an envelope of either ice or water vapor.
The ice canopy theory is rather bizarre and states that a past
work of Satan caused a gigantic atomic explosion. The result was a huge chunk of the earth being blown off into space
to become our moon! The resulting cavity is the Pacific
Ocean. The theory further states that as water was blown up
to cold altitudes, it froze into an ice canopy which surrounded the earth until the time of the flood. Falling dust
and debris are supposed to explain some of the rock layers.
Proponents of this theory think that later the ice melted and
furnished much of the water of the Noachian flood. Those

who propose the theory of a water-vapor canopy think that such a canopy might be what the Bible refers to as "the water above the firmament." If water vapor or ice had surrounded the earth, it might have given hothouse conditions which would explain the fact that fossils of tropical plants are found in coal deposits as far north as the Arctic Circle. Carcasses of frozen mammoths have been found in Siberia. People who accept this theory speculate that the descent of either the water or ice canopy would cause a rapid change in the climate and thus perhaps explain the frozen bodies of these animals.

CHANGE OF THE EARTH'S AXIS

Some people speculate that the earth was created with a vertical axis and that at the time of the flood the axis shifted to its present 23½ degrees of inclination. If so, it might have produced catastrophic changes at that time. This is an interesting supposition, but remember that it is only a theory, as are the others being presented.

CREATION IN 4004 B.C.

The date of 4004 B.C. was arrived at by Bishop James Ussher (1581-1656) who added together various dates from genealogical records in the Bible and used them as he would a calendar. Working at about the same time and using the same method, Lightfoot placed creation in the year 4004 B.C. This seventeenth century method of dating is not generally accepted now, for it is realized that in many places the Bible does not contain enough chronological material to be used as the basis for exact dating. Then, too, as shown near the end of chapter 14, Bible methods of speaking of family relationships are listed under the general headings of "son" so that sometimes it merely means "descendant"; "begat" may mean the "ancestor of"; the words "so-and-so" is the son of "so-and-so" may have long gaps between them (as in

Matt. 1:1); and some listings that may look like a father-son relationship are only giving the names of the head of a whole family or dynasty. These examples, showing the necessity for introducing into the genealogical records longer periods of time than was formerly thought necessary, have nothing to do with our belief in the Bible's inspiration. Ways of stating family relationships were different in Bible times, and the Bible is usually selective in the material it uses. Bible study since the time of Ussher has led people to suggest that his date for creation (4004 B.C.) may not be correct.

CREATION AT ABOUT 6000-15,000 B.C.

Dates for the earth's creation that roughly fall into the range of these numbers are accepted by many today. Especially during the last half century, as people studied the Bible and noted such facts as those listed previously, they realized that the date 4004 B.C. for the creation of the earth might be too recent. This conclusion was reached on the basis of Bible study alone without considering scientific dating methods. Many people who accept a young age for the earth have arrived at a date somewhere between 6000 and 15,000 B.C. as a result of restudying biblical genealogies.

THEISTIC EVOLUTION

A whole paper could be written about theistic evolution because there are so many variations in this school of thought. As the term implies, most theistic evolutionists combine a belief in a God who can work supernaturally with a belief in organic evolution. Most believe that God created original matter and the first living cell. From this cell, by powers resident within it and controlled by God, would have come an upward amoeba-to-man progressive evolution. Thus, as do other evolutionists, they believe that all of the plants and animals in the world are related.

According to this theory, some miraculous activity on the

part of God is usually included in connection with the appearance of man. Likely the most common idea is that man's physical body was the result of an evolutionary process but that at some place in history God put within it His spiritual likeness and at that time man possessed God's image.

DEISTIC EVOLUTION

Like the theistic evolutionist, people in this group believe in a personal God. Most of them think that He gave an original impetus to the created universe and then, as it were, stepped back and let things take their own course. The illustration often used is that God is One who "winds up a clock and lets it run itself."

FLOOD GEOLOGY

Some people are called flood geologists because they think that most of the rock strata and fossils were formed during the time of the Noachian flood. There is some difference of opinion within this group, but most feel that the "days" of Genesis were literal twenty-four-hour, consecutive days. They use the straight-line method of figuring genealogies and arrive at figures not too different from those of Ussher and Lightfoot. Most flood geologists feel that the earth was brought into existence as practically a smooth sphere. The liftings and foldings of the rocks, the shaping of most of the mountains and canyons, the formation of coal and oil would largely have taken place during the flood. They feel that the earth was created with a crust that was already cool, oceans that were salty when formed, and stars whose light had already reached the earth at the time it was brought into existence.

Very little credence is given to historical "age" geology or present-day dating methods. The Bibliography lists several books that show how flood geologists interpret the fossil strata.

SUMMARY

Realizing that the Bible is our one true and ultimate authority, we have listed some of man's interpretations of things related to creation. These theories or interpretations cannot all be true because God's Word has only one correct meaning. It is *this* meaning that Christian scientists are trying to find. As far as can be told at the present time, many details about creation, including a plain or clear explanation of the time when it took place, are not found in the written Word. This is because the Bible is selective in the material included, for God's main purpose in giving us the written Scripture is to set forth His plan of salvation. Keeping within the framework that the Word allows, created things are examined to see if some interpretation harmonizes the two.

We feel that there are definite weaknesses in each of the theories we have presented. Some are nonbiblical. Again let us be cautious not to accept any of them, even ours, merely because they are in print or because the author quotes from the Bible and is sincere in what he believes and writes.

We believe that the account given at the beginning of this chapter comes closest to harmonizing the scriptural account of the miraculous working of God with the facts of science.

The actual facts of creation about which we feel certain and can be dogmatic, are quite simple. In the beginning, a long time ago, God carried out definite creative acts which show a definite order or succession of events. After stating that He created the heaven and the earth, the rest of the creative account is concentrated on the earth because that most directly concerns man whom He was coming to redeem. Plants and animals were created "after their kind" and were fruitful and multiplied. God continued to fill and prepare the earth as a dwelling place for man and, when it satisfied Him, the last miraculous act before resting from His creative activity was to create man in His own image.

In this connection, in the first part of Genesis one sees more than just the fact that God created. Of course creation is seen here as well as in dozens of other places in the Bible, but the Bible very quickly moves on to its main theme of redemption and prophecies of the coming Saviour, the seed of the woman (Gen. 3:15). Redemption is also shown in type in the necessity for a blood sacrifice as seen when the Lord God made coats of skin to clothe Adam and Eve after they had sinned. Since the Bible is our standard of truth, when it and science are correctly interpreted, there can be no contradiction. As long as seeming contradictions exist, one should continue to study both of God's revelations, knowing that perfect harmony has to exist. James says "there is never the slightest variation or shadow of inconsistency" in God (James 1:17, Phillips).

16

What Is Meant by the Genesis Kind?

DID GOD CREATE each of the more than two hundred kinds of domesticated dogs? Did He create the Great Danes, the greyhounds, the collies, the shepherds, the bulldogs, the poodles and the Pekingese each one as we see it today? The evidence does not point to this. Even up until the time of the Middle Ages, many of those kinds of dogs did not exist. A fierce, wild dog was the most common one to roam the countryside and cities of medieval times. It appears that a wild dog such as this was ancestral to the present-day varieties like the ones just named.

But the next question is Did God create a "dog kind" that was ancestral not only to our present varieties of dogs but also to the wolf, jackal and coyote? To most scientists this latter choice seems to be the correct interpretation of the evidence. Refer again to Figure 3 to see what could have been the created kinds.

The Bible teaches and nature is in "agreement" with the view that God created certain groups of plants and animals and also established laws that allow changes to take place within these groups. These changes have taken place naturally, and some can be produced artificially by developing new breeds, varieties, subspecies, species, genera or, in some cases, apparently higher classification groups. All Christians, maybe without even realizing it, accept change on some of these levels. As mentioned, this must be done when one considers the kinds of human beings that have descended from Adam and Eve. Changes such as this are accepted within the lower classification groups. This in no way commits one to accept the kind of change between higher groups that would have been necessary for the theory of organic evolution to be true.

One must differentiate between the amount of change that is acceptable to the creationist and the amount that is not acceptable. Of course, the ground for judging this difference would be the Bible if it touched on each point—telling about each plant and animal. However, it does not go into specific detail in this area. The Bible says only that God created things "after their kind" or, as some translate it, "according to their subdivisions." What were these "subdivisions" or "kinds"? As indicated, they were not always the same as the word "species" or any one term in our man-made system of classification.

And what is a species? It is not possible to give a rigid definition but the following will be helpful. Members of a species are plants or animals, similar in structure and function, that do not usually breed with other species to produce offspring that are fertile. Members of different species are individuals that do not usually cross successfully with each other to produce vigorous offspring. It is in this sense that the word "species" will be used. In this definition we said organisms *usually* breed together because some plants and animals, which in their natural habitat will not interbreed, will interbreed if placed in artificial conditions. This is true of the mallard and pintail ducks.

In chapter 17 there is more about the reasons for saying that a definition of a species, similar to the one given here, is not rigid and is not a biblical term. A few illustrations will show the reason for being unable to point to each of the million and a half different species of plants and animals in the world today and dogmatically say, This is such-and-such a species. One needs to realize this because many sincere

people confuse speciation, or the development of new species, with the theory of evolution.

The genetic content of an individual cannot be told by
looking at its external characteristics. The two sexes of many
birds, like the peacock and turkey, are very different and yet
they belong to the same species. There are animals that at
different times in their life history look very different—as an
adult butterfly and its larva or pupa. Weasels that in many
locations are reddish-brown in color, in northern regions are
called ermines for in the winter they turn white. Individuals
that look different because of their sex, stage in life history,
or location are not the only confusing ones. The reverse may
be true, so plants and animals which look alike to the un-
trained eye may be members of entirely different species.
It is here that the work of a geneticist is especially useful. He
can tell that two individuals have had a common ancestor,
and tell something of the classification group in which they
belong, by showing that they have genes in common.

Look at a few more illustrations of why it is hard to give a
rigid definition of a species. In the Eastern United States
the common leopard frog, *Rana pipiens*, ranges from Vermont
to Texas. They freely breed with each other in all places
along this range and so clearly constitute a single species.
However, when the Vermont frogs are bred with the Texas
ones, they produce offspring that develop abnormally. The
genetic differences are great enough to prevent successful
hybrid formation. On this basis alone, one would be justified
in assigning them to separate species. However, knowing
their geographical distribution in this case suggests that they
all be retained in the same species. Such a case as this involving the leopard frog, gives evidence that species are
neither uniform nor unchanging groups of organisms. This
concept of change is even built into some definitions of a
species. One such definition is: "A species is a Mendelian

population which lives in a more or less extensive area and which gradually alters its genetic composition."

Luther Burbank's work makes one realize that he cannot say of a certain plant, as did Linnaeus back in 1758, "Since the time of creation it has remained the same and will stay unchanged until the end of time." Burbank crossed many plants to produce useful hybrids. He crossed the plum and apricot to produce a plumcot; a daisy from New England and one from Japan to get the beautiful Shasta daisy. The loganberry is a result of artificially crossing a blackberry and a raspberry.

Another good example for saying that a species is not a fixed entity, is the mule. A hybrid of a female horse (mare) and a male donkey (jackass) produced this animal with desirable work qualities. Every once in a while a fertile mule is produced, even though the parents belong to separate species. A hinny, the result of crossbreeding a male horse (stallion) with a female donkey (jenny) is not as desirable an animal as the mule.

One could continue to list many examples that are exceptions to our suggested definition of a species. A few more will be cited in chapter 17 where hybrids are discussed. The important thing to realize here is that because such things as Shasta daisies and loganberries can be produced, one cannot say that a species is a fixed entity. The unscientific term "fixity of species" has existed since the classification work done by Linnaeus in the middle of the eighteenth century. It is used by people who mistakenly think that the term "species" as used by Linnaeus is synonymus with the "kind" created by God. They do not realize that two species can be crossed to form new ones and that sometimes what was once thought of as one species should be divided into two or more.

There is no evidence that God separately created mules,

hinnies, plumcots, Shasta daisies or loganberries. Man has
both discovered and produced new plants and animals and is
continuing to add to the list of species named by Linnaeus.
A species is really anything but "fixed."

Returning to the question What are the kinds of Genesis?
one has to say that he does not know. The Bible does not say,
but it shows that God created certain groups of living things.
He surely did not create so many groups but what Adam
could give names to *all* so that "whatsoever Adam called
every living creature, that was the name thereof" (Gen.
2:19). It would take several years to examine each of the
animal species in existence today, even if one spent only a
few minutes on each and worked continuously day and night.
First Corinthians 15:39 (New Scofield) says: "All flesh is not
the same flesh, but there is one kind of flesh of men, another
flesh of beasts, another of fish, and another of birds." Genesis
lists a few more animals than these four groups. Nature
would indicate that God created many more major groups
than those listed in the Bible for we see around us certain
basic groupings or categories. These naturally occurring
groups are not always the same as any one division of our
man-made classification scheme. In some cases they appear
to be families, sometimes genera and, in some cases, species.
If these naturally occurring groups are the biblical kind,
they surely are not all listed in Scripture. One has to turn
to God's revelation in nature to learn more about them. These
groups can be recognized by the unbridged gaps that exist
on each side of them. At other places in this book these gaps
are mentioned as being the spaces unfilled by many missing
links. The existence of these hundreds of gaps is one of the
reasons for saying that nature shows a picture of creation
rather than an evolutionary graded series from simple to
complex organisms.

Do not be surprised when some change is made in the way
a plant or animal is classified, since change is involved in the

way a scientist must work. Work in classification is similar to the way Paul Ehrlich worked when he discovered the medicine "606" mentioned earlier. One should not stop with 605 experiments when the truth may be learned by the 606th.

By continual study Christian scientists are endeavoring to determine where the gaps should be placed and just which groups are the created kinds of Genesis. In chapter 17 some of the ways or methods by which these created kinds have undergone change are examined. As scientific creationists we cannot hold to fixity of species on the one hand or to evolution on the other. If one stays with the evidence after examining it, his faith in the authenticity of Scripture will be reaffirmed.

17

Things Do Change

GENETICS IS THE SCIENCE that deals with the study of heredity, the way characteristics are inherited from one generation to another. In this field many interesting things are being done which would have been impossible a few years ago, and what is done today may be outdated tomorrow. In organisms that usually reproduce by sexual means in the laboratory, the process of fertilization is being by-passed artificially. Carrots have been produced from only one parent. Instead of pollen grains, coconut milk has been used to cause the female cell to start developing. Frogs have been produced by removing the nucleus from an unfertilized egg and replacing it with the nucleus from an intestinal cell of a tadpole. The egg then develops, and the resulting individual is like the tadpole from which the nucleus came. In rats, work has been done to try to find out why some are bright and some are stupid. Before birth, rats have been treated with pituitary extract causing the growth of more than the normal amount of brain tissue.

Amazing things can be done with human beings. In fact, a whole new science called "fetology" is being developed. Before birth a blood transfusion can be given to a fetus whose blood has an Rh factor incompatible with that of the mother. This has resulted in saving a large percentage of the babies who would not otherwise have been able to survive birth. There are many genetic diseases, such as galactosemia, in which the child cannot digest the galactose in milk. If untreated, the child may develop such things as cataracts and cirrhosis of the liver. If the condition is detected early enough its adverse effect may be prevented. A number of genetic diseases can be detected before birth and treated before they really become established in the baby.

This field of genetics not only is interesting but also is important in our study of evolution. In the first part of this book are many examples of the changes that take place in plants and animals. We now will try to answer the following questions: (1) What are the reasons for changes that take place? (2) How much change can take place? (3) Are the changes enough to account for the process of organic evolution? If evolution is true, there must be some mechanism by which it could come about. For this reason, genetics is one of the most crucial areas we have considered.

EVOLUTIONARY INTERPRETATION

The evolutionist says that changes in living things are great enough to have allowed *all* of them to have come from one original cell. In advanced texts it is sometimes suggested that the occurrence of spontaneous generation is not unique. The following quotation is typical of most high school books:

> Assuming that life has arisen only once on the earth, the 1.7 million known species of protists, plants, and animals living today (not to mention all the species that have become extinct) must have arisen from ancestors that they shared in common.[1]

This quotation is from Kimball who then goes on to say that this concept of evolution was advanced before the time of Darwin but that he was the one "who built a virtually airtight case for the idea and then proposed natural selection to explain how evolution works." As do most of our authors, Kimball discusses how changes arise by means of such things as hybrids, mutations, and recombinations of chromosomes. He concludes that natural selection acting on these changes is sufficient to account for the origin of new species. No men-

[1] J. W. Kimball, *Biology*, p. 567.

tion is made of any method by which any of the larger classification groups could have been produced. Another book
gives a similar explanation of the way in which evolution
might have taken place, but the discussion is only of methods
that can be applied to the origin of new species; a few suggest new genera.

> The theory of natural selection is accepted today as
> the explanation of the mechanism of evolution. Organ-
> isms overproduce, then struggle to survive. . . . Organ-
> isms with unfavorable variations are eventually elimi-
> nated because they do not survive and reproduce.
> Natural selection results in better adaptation to ever
> changing environments, hence in new species.[2]

Some high school texts are very dogmatic in saying that the
question of the method by which evolution took place has
been solved. This quotation shows that all authors are not
so sure of this:

> Biologists are not in complete agreement about how
> evolution could occur. Darwin's theory of how species
> originate was modified by DeVries; in that form it is
> rather generally accepted.[3]

CREATIONIST INTERPRETATION

Looking back into history, one finds that many of our con-
cepts about the amount and kind of change that can take
place in plants and animals began with the work of Gregor
Mendel. About the middle of the nineteenth century he performed many experiments with garden peas. They were not
then called chromosomes or genes, but he first determined
the existence of hereditary units. Mendel formulated various
laws that explained how these hereditary units were transmitted from generation to generation. Other scientists have
built upon the foundation laid by Mendel.

[2]W. H. Gregory and E. H. Goldman, *Biological Science*, p. 733.
[3]E. Kroeber, W. H. Wolff, and R. L. Weaver, *Biology*, p. 493.

Much is being learned about heredity by studying chemical substances known as nucleic acids. Deoxyribonucleic acid, usually referred to as DNA, carries hereditary information. In combination with protein, it makes up a large part of the chromosomes. It is thought that genes are localized parts of chromosomes made up of a molecule or part of a molecule of DNA. This would make it the ultimate hereditary material and so be the substance that really determines what you are. The molecule is a complicated one made up of two interlocking strands arranged in a double helical structure with crossbars as explained on page 102. Figure 7 shows this pictorially.

There are millions of kinds of DNA molecules for they are capable of much variation. Those in the nucleus of a person's cells are different from those of every other person except in the case of identical twins. During ordinary cell division they make exact copies or replicas of themselves so that every new cell is just like the one from which it came. In this way identical characteristics are passed on to each cell in one's body, whether it be nerve or bone, muscle or tendon. What is the source of these genes?

As noted, genes are located on the chromosomes in the nucleus of a cell. Each living thing has its own specific number of chromosomes. Germ cells are made in the reproductive organs. While the germ cells are growing to maturity they go through a process of reduction division so that half the original number of chromosomes is found in a mature egg or sperm. When they unite during fertilization, the original number of chromosomes again is restored. In this way half of the chromosomes come from each parent and yet the number is kept the same from generation to generation. Against this background, consider some of the ways that have been proposed to account for the changes that do take place in living things.

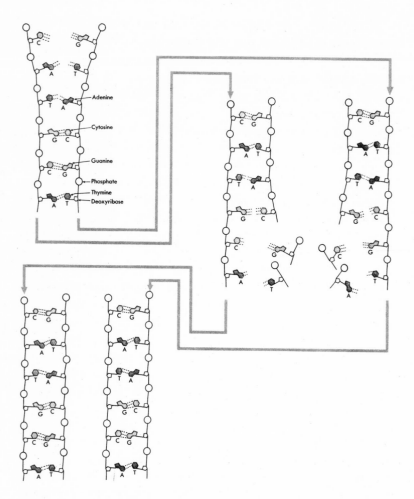

Figure 7

A diagram of the way a DNA molecule may duplicate itself so that each body cell contains the same kind as every other cell. From *Biology* by John Kimball, copyright © 1965 by Addison-Wesley. Reprinted by permission of the publisher.

Lamarck's Theory

Historically, Lamarck's theory was one of the first. It is commonly called the "use and disuse theory" or the "inheritance of acquired characteristics." The illustration of a blacksmith's right arm is often given to explain this theory. Because the blacksmith uses his arm continually, his arm muscles grow powerful and larger. Lamarck decided that the use of a particular organ, if continued for several generations, would cause it gradually to become changed. In this way the blacksmith's descendants would have larger and more powerful right-arm muscles. Lamarck, who thought that the ancestors of the giraffes stretched their necks to reach the leaves in the higher parts of the trees, concluded that after many generations of such stretching, long-necked giraffes evolved.

The basic fallacy of Lamarck's theory is that acquired characteristics are not inherited! Many high school books tell of August Weismann's work that casts doubt upon Lamarck's theory. He cut off the tails of new born mice for twenty generations. The tails of the mice of the twenty-first generation were just as long as those of the first generation. Removing the tails affected the body cells but had no influence upon reproductive cells. Most scientists today do not hold to Lamarck's concept of the inheritance of acquired characteristics.

Darwin's Theory

Darwin's theory is characterized by the phrases "struggle for existence" and "survival of the fittest." As he originally presented the theory, it stated that living beings contended with each other for food and life's necessities. In this struggle he said that the weak die and the strong live with the total pattern leading to stronger and better plants and animals. His theory would explain the giraffe's long neck by saying neck lengths vary in any population. The long-necked individuals compete more successfully for food since they can reach the higher branches. They survive and transmit the long neck to their offspring, while the shorter-necked giraffes die because there is a limited food supply for them. Thus the unfavorable trait (in this case the short neck) in time would disappear. It is true that by natural selection, characteristics that improve the chances of an organism surviving and reproducing are often accentuated. The organism may become better adapted to live in some particular environment. However, unless combined with another process, selection alone cannot initiate new qualitative changes.

Darwin observed variations, but had no real explanations for them. There were many things about genetics that were not known in his day. He thought that a characteristic which did not show in an individual, did not survive, and in time would disappear. He did not know that there were such things as recessive genes. Such a gene, even though not visible, may be carried along on the chromosomes for many generations. Darwin did not realize that evolution could take place only if new genes were formed to control increasingly complex activities. He thought that there could be unlimited change in all directions, not knowing that change can take place only within strict limits.

All scientists agree that selection is an important cause of change and much has been learned about it by performing experiments in artificial conditions. Artificial selection of desirable plants and animals is a method man has used for centuries. He can develop a herd of cattle to suit his particular purpose because for breeding he may choose cows that produce a large quantity of milk with a high butterfat content, or ones with good beef qualities. With dogs he may select and breed those with either speed and endurance or beauty and intelligence. In recent years, through selection carried out for several generations, turkeys have been developed to secure birds that suit the needs of small families. Pigs also have been selected to produce small rather than large ones.

It is sometimes desirable to use pigs in laboratory experiments, but their large size is unhandy. In about five years time, by selection, it was possible to reduce the weight of the average hog from 600 to 150 or 180 pounds.

In thinking about Darwin's theory and the whole area of natural or artificial selection, there are several things to consider. First, there are many situations in nature where no struggle for existence is found. Second, the fittest are not always the ones to survive; sometimes the weak and sickly are better cared for and given extra protection. Third, where these two conditions, struggle and survival, are found and better individuals are produced, they are still the same kind of individuals. As one author says, new kinds of organisms are not formed by survival alone for it merely separates the fit from the unfit. Remember that natural selection can work only on that which already exists; it cannot originate. We emphasize this because some of our high school books say that natural selection is the chief means by which evolution takes place. "The theory of natural selection is accepted today as the explanation of the mechanism of evolution." While it is true that some high school books combine the idea with other causes of change as is shown in the next section about mutations, selection is usually listed as the principle cause of evolution. This cannot be true for it causes change only within groups and not between the ones that would be necessary for amoeba-to-man evolution to have taken place.

DeVries' Theory

DeVries' theory, an account of which is found in almost all high school biology texts, is the third one to be considered. The key word is "mutations." Long before anything was known of the mechanism of heredity, people noted different and unusual individuals appearing in a population and called them "sports." Some of the best known mutations are the seedless orange and grape, the short-legged Ancon sheep, hornless cattle, albino animals and plants without chlorophyll.

Let us explain mutations in terms of a DNA molecule. As noted, when a cell divides, each DNA molecule duplicates itself accurately and continues to do so in the same way millions of times as cell division continues. This usually happens without a mistake, for the molecule is a very stable one. Occasionally an error takes place. A different nucleotide is put into the molecule or one is left out. This change in the molecule modifies it so that it is no longer an exact copy of the original. The change is a permanent one which affects the genetic message to other cells, and so the individuals of the next generation are different from those of the last. A change in the genetic message is called a mutation.

Knowledge of mutations is increased by studying new ones that have been produced artificially. There are factors that can be applied to a nucleic acid molecule to make it mutate more easily, and the changed condition is faithfully transmitted into other cells and individuals. These factors are often worked with experimentally in the laboratory to produce new mutations. The most common technique is to treat the reproductive cells with external agents such as temperature, chemicals or irradiation. (1) If the reproductive cells will tolerate an increase in temperature, mutations are produced at a higher rate. (2) When the reproductive cells are treated with such chemicals as colchicine, mustard gas, formaldehyde or peroxide, more mutations are formed. (3) Mutations are often produced when the cells are subjected to high-energy radiation as x rays, beta or gamma rays, radium emanations or ultraviolet light. With microbeams it is possible to irradiate only the nucleus of a cell. Evolutionists today consider mutations one of the most important cornerstones of their theory. The factors mentioned in the above paragraph may cause one of several things to happen within the nucleus of the cell: (1) There may be a change in the number of chromosomes so that a set is doubled, tripled, etc. This condition is called polyploidy. (2) There may be a change in the chromosomes themselves as when a piece breaks loose and then fuses onto another chromosome or fuses with the original one but in an inverted position. These are called crossing over and inversion. (3) There may be the accidental loss or addition of a whole chromosome. (4) There may be a change in the chemical nature of a chromosome. These four kinds of changes are called chromosome mutations, but there are also "point mutations" or changes in a single gene. Both of these kinds of changes breed true to type and so they are passed on to the next generation. The evolutionary authors of most high school biology texts list mutations, combined with natural selection, as the chief way by which they think evolution could have taken place. What are the weaknesses of this line of reasoning?

First, one must realize that most mutations occurring in the same environment are harmful rather than helpful. This, of course, is looking at the situation from the viewpoint of the plant or animal involved and not from that of man. If the Ancon sheep had not been protected by man, it would have fallen prey to its speedier enemies because its short legs handicapped it in running and jumping. Hornless cattle, in the same way, have lost one of their best means of protecting themselves against their enemies. The seedless orange, although beneficial to man, would have been fatal to the continued existence of that plant if man had not propagated it by grafting. The same is true of one of the mutations of the evening primrose which produced only female offspring. In fruit flies there are many dozens of mutations causing usually harmful conditions such as deformed wings and legs, absence of eyes, reduction of the area of eye vision or of its amount of pigment.

A second fact that must be recognized is that naturally occurring mutations are not a common occurrence. In spite of the fact that some genes may mutate more frequently than others, the chance of this change taking place in any one gene is rare. This is especially true of the helpful ones, for there are some that are beneficial in a particular environment. It is hard to imagine that, even allowing an immense amount of time, there could have been a large enough percentage of helpful ones in the past to have contributed much to an evolutionary process.

Besides usually being harmful and rare, a third consideration concerning mutations is that they occur at random and are very unpredictable. They do not follow a fixed direction as would be necessary if amoeba-to-man evolution were true. In neither nature nor the laboratory is it possible to fully foretell what will be the result of subjecting the chromosomes of a cell to heat, chemicals or radiation.

The last point concerning mutations relates to the fact that they are usually recessive and so cannot be seen in an individual. Unless a person has two genes, one from each parent, the characteristic will not be observable. One may well ask how an individual can get two similar genes so that a recessive characteristic will show. There are two ways. The first and unlikely one is that the same mutation would have occurred in each parent at the same time. A more likely possibility is that the parents each received them from a common ancestor. In this way, a recessive mutation might show up if there was mating between close relatives. This is one of the reasons that many states have laws against certain close relatives marrying each other. Cooley's anemia is a genetic disease caused by a recessive gene. If an individual has only one gene, he may seem to be normal because the gene for the disease is hidden. Suppose there were two cousins, each of whom has received a recessive gene for Cooley's anemia from a common ancestor. If they should marry, there would be the possibility that some of their children might receive one of these defective genes from each parent; therefore the children would have this disease, which usually proves to be fatal.

It is hard to see how mutations could account for evolution unless there was some direction toward a determined goal. The theory of evolution does not allow for the existence of purposefulness. It seems contradictory that one continually finds references to certain things developing "in response to the need" for that particular thing.

In a chapter titled "Genetic Adaptation: Evolution" the BSCS Green Version gives another such illustration. The book is completely evolutionary in its approach and yet it says:

> Evolution is neither a great number of changes taking place all at once nor a random change. Rather, it is a guided, selective change, with environmental factors . . . usually playing a part in the selection. Thus there is also a *guiding factor* in evolution.[4]

A consistent, completely evolutionary position does not allow for the existence of a *guiding factor*. We feel that this is another weakness in the theory of evolution. The Christian sees creation and a guiding and sustaining force coming from the hand of God, and he gladly acknowledges that "all things are held together in him" (Col. 1:17, NEB).

Three theories, proposed in the past to account for the way evolution might have taken place, have been examined. Lamarck's is not acceptable because acquired characteristics are not inherited. Darwin's theory of selection, either natural or artificial, accounts for considerable change, but only as it works on changes originated by some other method. Also, these changes are only between specific barriers. DeVries' mutation theory also explains some change, but mutations are rather rare, usually harmful and recessive, and take place

---

[4]Biological Science Curriculum Study, *High School Biology: BSCS Green Version*, p. 585.

in random directions—again, only within and not between the groups that we believe are the kinds spoken of in Genesis.

Most evolutionists today would not say that any one of these three theories is sufficient to account for evolution. Instead they say there is a combination of elements from two or more different theories. The most frequently combined ones are natural selection working on mutations. One must recognize that these two processes cause considerable change, but we will examine some examples to see if this change is great enough to ever cause one large classification group to become another. Are the differences produced ever more than minor ones within a limited group? Hemophilia, or bleeders disease, is a mutation that occasionally arises spontaneously. It is thought that Queen Victoria was the victim of such a mutation. Although it was not harmful to her, it appeared in some of her offspring, mostly the males. Natural selection acted on this harmful mutation to cause the premature death of some of her descendants.

The case of hemophilia is similar to other mutations already mentioned. The principle of the fittest surviving in the struggle for existence would eliminate the short-legged rams, the seedless plants and the hornless animals, if not preserved by man. These malformed individuals tend to be killed by natural enemies, disease, starvation or some other factor. Most scientists agree that the largest number of mutations appearing today are harmful and often die as the result of natural selection. Therefore, these two factors working together usually do not give the kind of improved condition needed for the process of evolution to have taken place.

Next we will consider whether natural selection ever does preserve helpful variations.

The change that has taken place in the moth *Biston betularis,* in the industrial regions around Manchester, England, is a notable example. These high-colored, peppered moths are most active at night. In the daytime, while resting on light-colored tree trunks, they are well camouflaged. Darker moths are more easily spotted and eaten by birds. During the past century, as tree trunks in this section of England became darkened by industrial smoke, it was noted that there was a shift in the color of the moth population. From a small percentage of dark moths in relation to light ones, there developed a larger percentage of dark ones.

To be sure of what was happening, experiments were performed. Scientists put an equal number of light and dark moths on a *dark* tree trunk and watched the birds more often catch and eat the light-colored moths. When an equal number of light and dark moths were put on a *light* tree trunk, the opposite was the case, it was the dark moths that were more quickly picked off by the birds. It seems reasonable to conclude that this nonharmful, inheritable variation, when acted on by natural selection, has become helpful to the moth by increasing its chances of survival. In this illustration the environment of the moth changed. The number of dark moths increased as the number of smoke-darkened trees increased.

We recognize that natural selection, acting on variations in a local population, such as this of the moths, can cause considerable change in that population. But, is this in any way evidence to be used in support for the theory of evolution? Our answer is a definite no. We see change, but not the kind needed as a method by which organic evolution could take place. It is a crucial point to realize that this is not the kind of change needed to account for evolution. One of our books calls this change in the color of moths a "miniature but true example of evolution." We cannot agree. In this book the word "evolution" is used to refer to change that could have caused an original spontaneously generated cell to have developed into all of the kinds of plants and animals in the world today. Within the limits of this concept, change in the color of moths is not a miniature picture of evolution. We acknowledge the fact that these moths undergo an heredity change. However, evidence does not point to the fact that this kind of change is significant enough to be considered as organic evolution. It is not the kind of change that would have bridged the gaps between large category groups as necessitated by the theory of evolution.

There are other simple ways of producing a change in the members of a population—ways that should not be confused with evolution. Consider an illustration of the way migration may cause change. One high school book suggests that one supposes an area containing long- and short-haired dogs. If for some reason the long-haired dogs migrate to a different area, a population largely made up of short-haired dogs would be left.

Isolation is another factor that produces change. It is often found associated with migration as is noted in chapter 8 about geographic distribution. If the long- and short-haired dogs become separated by a barrier, in time the gene pool of each group of dogs may readjust, each along different lines. There is change but not evolution. The dogs are still dogs.

Recall that it was mentioned earlier that isolation may be caused by other than geographic barriers. There are also ecological barriers, behavioral-pattern ones, different court-ship barriers, time barriers and ones caused by extreme differences in size. It is easy to recognize in dogs what is meant by saying that a difference in size may isolate one population from another. Great Danes and Pekingese, even though living in the same geographical location, will remain isolated from each other since they usually do not interbreed.

Hybrids such as the mule and hinny, the Shasta daisy and loganberry, were mentioned in chapter 16. In this chapter about how things do change, are listed a few more hybrids, since this is such a common way of producing desirable changes in plants and animals. To produce superior beef cattle that can endure heat, are resistant to insect pests, and will grow rapidly, Aberdeen Angus cattle have been crossed with the Brahman bull from India.

A hybrid with superior body type and more wool has been produced by crossing a purebred ram with a Navajo ewe.

In some places cattaloes are prized for meat and their large size. They are produced by crossing cows with male buffaloes. It is interesting to note that cattalo females are fertile while the males are sterile. Often hybrids are sterile because the two parents have different numbers or kinds of chromosomes which cannot come together in pairs as they do in normal cell division. Sometimes, however, hybrids have been produced with a double set of chromosomes, or even three or four times the usual number. This already has been mentioned under the term "polyploidy." Some examples of desirable polyploid hybrids are cultivated wheat, corn, marigolds and larkspur.

Hybridization that results in polyploidy also has produced new species for which we have no special use. The first artificially produced new species was made in 1928 by Karpechenko, a Russian geneticist who crossed a radish and a cabbage. Some call the new plant a "rabbage." In the second generation it has a full set of chromosomes from both the radish and cabbage and this polyploid condition yields a vigorous plant. Unfortunately this plant has a root like a cabbage, spindly and inedible, and leaves like a radish, prickly and useless! The plants will breed successfully with one another but not with either ancestral type.

The "rabbage" illustrates the fact that new species have been brought into existence. This new thing is not to be thought of as evolutionary advance as the term "evolution" is used in this book. The BSCS Green Version says about the "rabbage," "It is one of man's greatest evolutionary triumphs," but the creationist does not see it as such. Just because it might be helpful to the evolutionary theory, it is wishful thinking for anyone to extend to all of the major classification groups the kind of change seen in minor groups. Evolution is not established or confirmed because a "rabbage" or any other new species can be produced. Neither is it established because hybrids can be produced between plants and animals of different genera. The yak is a long-haired member of the cattle family found in Tibet and high mountain regions of Asia. Most zoologists place it in a separate genus from domestic cattle. Hybrids between yak and cattle are often crossed to produce a breed commonly raised in this part of the world.

Another example of the origin of a genus is a sea otter found along the California coast. It has webbed toes and spends much of its time in the water. The common otter is placed in a separate genus but the two will crossbreed and produce a different kind of offspring.

For organic evolution to take place there must be a method or combination of methods by which higher classification groups such as phyla, classes and orders can originate. Evidence does not point to the existence of such a method and this is one reason for believing that these groups were separately created by God. Some high school books, after discussing the origin of species and genera, for which we can see evidence and therefore agree, extend these same methods into the field of theory but fail to emphasize that it *is* only a theory. It is said that these methods could account for change between *all* categories and therefore explain the way the theory of organic evolution could have taken place. We cannot agree with this. If a person starts with the preconceived idea that evolution is a satisfactory theory, then, and then only can he believe and say that these processes that cause demonstrable change could be extended and counted responsible for *all* the change needed to validate the theory of evolution.

Even allowing long periods of time is not a critical factor. One of our books, in speaking of the theoretical origin of higher categories says, "Such events are almost certain to take place during the long ages of evolutionary time."[5] More time will not bring into existence a process that does not exist! A process that could explain organic evolution has not been observed in nature or in the laboratory. Neither is there evidence in the geological record for the existence of such a method.

In summary we acknowledge that things do change. As creationists we say that there is nothing in genetics to contradict what we read in Genesis. Except for man, the Bible does not tell us about the creation of individual organisms, but rather of groups that were created after their kind. We see today, as with man, enough variation within the limits of these groups to produce considerable diversification.

The cause of this diversification can be explained on the basis of hereditary laws that have been discussed. God set into operation natural laws connected with such things as mutations, polyploidy, selection, hybridization, isolation, migration and chromosome rearrangement. We do not confuse these changes with evolution. We are thankful that we have and can know the one true God who is not only the Creator but who also has allowed enough change to produce the variety of living things with which we are surrounded. "He hath made every thing beautiful in his time" (Eccles. 3:11).

[5]BSCS, *Biological Science: An Inquiry into Life*, Yellow Version, p. 632.

18

Complicated Chromosomes

A DNA MOLECULE is so complicated that some people find it difficult to understand its intricacies. A little has been told already about our present-day knowledge concerning it. It is easy to become confused, for in describing a single molecule such terms are used as thymine, guanine, adenine, cytosine, purines, pyrimidines, deoxyribose, nucleic acid, nucleotides and phosphate. It is fitting to say that the chromosomes, made up of this material, are very, very complicated. Do you realize the implications when one says that a gene is a DNA molecule, or maybe only part of one?

EVOLUTIONARY INTERPRETATION

At the high school level students are told that evolution can remodel and build only upon what already exists. This would lead to the conclusion that all genetic material capable of producing even the most complex organisms was present in the first living cell. The theory teaches that this first cell was generated spontaneously. It would have had to contain all the potential material necessary to produce over a million and a half different species, including man. Is it logical to suppose that the DNA material within the chromosomes was all present in this original cell? Could it have contained all that was necessary to develop into the mosses, ferns, grasses, trees, insects, reptiles, birds, mammals and every other living thing? Consider the following quotation from one of the high school texts and see if this is not the conclusion at which one must arrive:

> Clearly, evolution can only remodel and build on what already exists, in small successive steps. Since, given a

long enough time span, *every* feature of *every* organism undergoes random variations in many different directions, opportunities for diverse evolutionary changes have been and still are very numerous. . . . Therefore, every organism, man not excepted, is a patchwork of good opportunities seized by selection at the right time. . . . We consequently conclude that specific organisms are *not* the result of any planned, goal-directed, or predetermined course of creation. Instead, they are the result of a cumulative, opportunistic process of piece-by-piece building based on preexisting organisms.[1]

CREATIONIST INTERPRETATION

Now think about the complicated chromosomes that are made up of this complex DNA material. Is it logical to think that these complex molecules could have been generated spontaneously? This is the conclusion at which one must arrive if he says that all genetic material of each generation had to be present in the ancestors of that generation. If one extends this principle back into all past ages, according to the theory of evolution, he eventually arrives at a cell which supposedly became alive spontaneously by the chance coming together of inorganic materials. It is impossible to imagine such complicated material, by chance alone, ever coming together and forming itself into DNA molecules and thus into genes and chromosomes. Even though this is the direction into which this line of reasoning leads us, most authors of the texts being considered cite some place in the evolutionary scale where a cell does not contain *all* of the potential material that could be responsible for an indefinite amount of change. For instance, one book says:

> It might have been adaptively exceedingly useful for terrestrial plants to grow legs or for terrestrial animals to grow wheels, but neither occurred, because it could not

[1]P. B. Weisz, *The Science of Biology*, p. 715.

occur. The ancestors simply did not possess the necessary structural and functional potential.[2]
It is not a foolish question to ask why legs on plants and
wheels on animals could not have been produced. If resident
within an original cell was the capacity to produce something
as complicated as the human eye, why could there not also
have been the potential to produce these things?

Another author gives a similar illustration when he says
that the little fruit fly *Drosophila melanogaster* has no way
to produce green or blue eyes. By known hereditary laws, it
is possible to secure from the wild red eye such colors as
claret, white, garnet, vermillion, cardinal, maroon, pink, scar-
let, sepia, carnation, purple, cinnebar, brown, ruby and raspberry. As far as we know, green or blue eyes never have and
are not likely to be produced. If evolution is true, why should
not these colors appear? It is a simple answer. DNA molecules with the sequence of bases capable of producing these
colors do not exist in fruit flies. If the chromosomes of an
original cell did not contain all of the DNA necessary to produce all of the tissues, organs and systems of all living things,
what other possibility exists? One has to answer this by saying that according to the theory of evolution, there would
have had to be some process by which genetic material could
have been added to a cell. As seen in chapter 17, a great deal
of change can take place within the nuclei of cells. It was
shown that by polyploidy the number of chromosomes may
be multiplied. By hybridization, two quite different kinds of
chromosomes can be combined into one cell. In mutations,
the DNA is altered in different ways and by different methods. After a population has migrated, its gene frequency can
be changed. By chromosome rearrangements, such as inversion and crossing over, individuals differing from their parents can be produced. Selection can act on these and other
changes to eliminate the less fit and preserve those best fitted
to live in a particular environment. However, in none of
[2]*Ibid.*, p. 714.

these cases can new DNA material that did not previously exist be added to a chromosome and so actually enter a cell. This fact leaves the evolutionist with an unanswered question. The creationist sees the answer in the biblical account of creation where are found listed the kinds of groups of plants and animals that God miraculously brought into existence. He also established methods by which change could take place within these groups. No amount of time, even billions of years, can alter this God-made arrangement. Now consider chromosomes as a whole rather than the genes and DNA material of which they are made. The evolutionist accepts the idea that "animals vary in complexity from amoeba to man. Plants vary in complexity from single-celled algae to multicelled flowering plants."[3] If it were true that living things had evolved in this order, would it not also be reasonable to expect to see a gradual increase in genetic material as plants and animals become more complex? Should not this gradual increase in complexity show in an increase in the number of genes and also in the number of chromosomes that contain this genetic material? Is it not logical to suppose that their number would be less in the simple organisms and more in the complex ones? The size of the chromosomes and the number of genes contained must also be considered; but if evolution were true, might one not expect to see new chromosomes added as one ascends the plant and animal scale? This is surely not the case.

Selected species of the following plants and animals are arranged approximately in order as they are said to have evolved:

Name of some plants	Chromosomes in body cells
an algae	48
another algae	24
a moss	40

[3]W. H. Gregory and E. H. Goldman, *Biological Science*, p. 661.

a fern	28
pine	24
onion	16
a lily	48
trillium	24
radish	9
red clover	14
alsike clover	8
tobacco	96
peas	14

Name of some animals

radiolarian	1,600
certain roundworms	2
earthworm	36
snail	200, 208
housefly	12
fruitfly	8
trout	80, 84
chicken	78
rabbit	44
fox	34
horse	64
cattle	60
man	46

Most chromosome numbers are between ten and fifty. Ones above or below that number are rare. In flies the number is unusually low and in birds it is unusually high. There seems to be little relationship between the number of chromosomes and the complexity of the species. Often very closely related organisms will have very different numbers of chromosomes.

We certainly do not see a general increase in chromosome numbers to correspond with the general increase in complexity of the organism. This is one more difficulty to add to our list of reasons for not accepting the theory of evolution. We come back again to the conclusion that evolution is not a fact and that "in the beginning God *created*. . . ."

19

What's in It for You?

THIS IS A VERY PERSONAL CHAPTER. It will call for a decision from the reader. All the truths previously presented, if carefully considered, lead one to the place where he must decide what he as an individual believes about evolution and/or creation.

Young people today stand at a very puzzling place in their lives and in history. Behind them have marched the heroes of the faith who never heard of the Neanderthal man, an atom or DNA. Theirs was an unquestioning faith in the Bible as the very Word of God. Many were reared in godly homes where from earliest childhood the Bible was read, taught, believed and lived. They came to an early personal regenerating faith in Christ, and no text or teacher drove a wedge of doubt into their trusting minds.

But now they find themselves in the midst of an oftentimes professing but powerless group of young people, many of whom have accepted a pseudoscience that gives no answer to the vital questions that face them. They want to know whether the Bible is really the Word of God. They have the right to know. Their hearts and minds cry out for the truth while around them swirl the winds and storms of doubt, honest questing and scientific theories. Is the Bible merely one of a number of sacred books? Does it contain errors? What is truth? This was answered once for all when Christ said, "I am the way, the truth, and the life" (John 14:6).

How can one know whether the Bible is the Word of God? One reason is that it has stood the acid test of time. Other

books have periods of popularity but the Bible is always
being printed and read by multitudes. Year after year it continues to be the world's best seller. The Bible is composed
of sixty-six books written by forty or more different human
instruments. "Men moved by the Holy Spirit spoke from
God" (II Peter 1:21*b*, RSV). Long periods of time separated
the writing of one portion from another, yet a unity of theme
and purpose exists that only a single mind could have main-
tained. The sacrifices of the Old Testament are fulfilled in
the death of Christ on the cross, the law of Exodus is explained in Galatians, Leviticus blossoms in Hebrews, and
Isaiah paints the portrait of the Christ who walks through
the Gospels.

The Bible contains enough fulfilled prophecy to stagger the
mind and cause the unbeliever truly to wonder. It is only
because it is God-breathed that this is true.

Augustus on his throne in Rome had no idea that he was
fulfilling God's Word when he commanded that each man
go to the city of his birth to be taxed. In this way, at the
very moment in time when Mary was to bring into the world
the virgin-born, only begotten Son of God, she was at the
place of God's choosing. The scribes in Jerusalem knew the
place of Christ's birth to tell to the wise men, for the Lord
had revealed it to Micah hundreds of years before. The flight
into Egypt and the years spent in Nazareth were all foretold
before they happened.

Thus it was said of one Man, Jesus, that He was to be born
in Bethlehem, to come forth out of Egypt and yet be called
a Nazarene. It is said that there are more than two thousand
prophecies concerning Christ alone. There is only one possibility in billions that these could all be fulfilled in the life of
one man.

Fulfilled prophecies concerning the resurrection alone, give
credence to the entire gospel story. But "if there be no resurrection of the dead, then is Christ not risen: and if Christ

be not risen, then is our preaching vain, and your faith is also vain. But now *is* Christ risen from the dead" (I Cor. 15:13-14, 20).

The Jew is a sad and constant witness to the fact that the Bible is the supernatural Word of God. When Christ was crucified, the Jews said that His blood could be upon their head and upon those of their children. For almost two millenniums these persecuted people were as strangers out of their native land and as a byword among the nations. It is surely a miracle to see the way their identity as a race has been preserved in spite of such things as the gas chambers of World War II. Attesting to the truth of Scripture, in 1948 Israel was admitted to the family of nations. Since then a constant chain of events points toward the time when the Jews will recognize Christ as their Messiah and King.

Is the Bible a supernatural book? Consider the fact that wherever it has gone civilization and progress have followed. Hospitals, education, freedom, decency, law and order are by-products of the Bible.

Another way that the Bible is seen to be a supernatural Book is in its power to impart life to a dead soul. "The entrance of thy words giveth light" (Ps. 119:130). "And that from childhood you have known the sacred Scriptures which can give you wisdom that leads to salvation through the faith that leans on Christ Jesus" (II Tim. 3:15, Williams). A single Bible verse can be used of God to lead a soul to a saving knowledge of the Saviour.

After a soul is saved, Bible reading and a real belief in what has been read can transform a life. Old things pass away as the Word takes its rightful place. Billy Sunday left his baseball for the privilege of preaching to hungry souls. Moody let someone else sell shoes while he won thousands to the Lord. Mary Slessor lived on in Africa after supplies were gone because she loved the Africans and saw the gospel changing lives. Widows of martyred men continued to teach

the very Auca Indians who had murdered their husbands.
Billy Graham's time and talents have been used to win multitudes to the Lord.

The central theme of the Bible is the Lord Jesus Christ.
What one thinks of Him and does with Him are the most
important decisions in your life. Time is but a speck between
two eternities. One life is only a very small part of that time.
When the few years of a lifetime have run their course, then
what happens? Deep within the human heart lies a God-
given knowledge that the soul lives on after the body dies.
Immortality is woven into the very fabric of the human being.
Christ offers the only true answer to the question of one's
future abode and condition after death.

No sincerity of belief in a dead doctrine or a false religion
can impart life. Life comes from life. Spiritual life comes
from God through Christ. "And this is life eternal, that they
might know thee the only true God, and Jesus Christ, whom
thou hast sent" (John 17:3). There is one way—Christ. He
is the door into eternal, blessed and joyful life. How futile to
grope blindly about a solid wall of untruth and doubt when
an open door surely leads to heaven! How sad to try to climb
up some other way when one way is always open! How
foolish to concoct theories and new religions when truth
beckons with nail-pierced hands!

Look now to Christ. Question yourself honestly. At this
very time you may decide where you will spend eternity.
Yes, you are the one who must decide. What do you think
of Christ? Was He the virgin-born Man He claimed to be?
Was His life without blemish or spot? Was He God in the
flesh? Does His blood atone for sin? Did He die in your
place? Have you ever accepted Him as your Saviour? If not,
will you not do this now?

Do you think the way is narrow? You want something
real, vital and of eternal value. You want a personal relationship with God. There is one way to accomplish your desire—

through Christ. The way *is* narrow; it excludes all that is false. Truth is always narrow, otherwise falsehood would enter and destroy. Bridges are narrow ways but they span engulfing floods. Sin would swallow us up and keep us from the true way, but there is a bridge—Christ Himself. Doors look small when they are in huge walls but they open into places of safety and rest. Come in through God's door, even Christ, and you will find rest and safety for your soul for time and eternity.

Look now to Him. By an act of simple faith you may be born into the family of God by telling Him you believe that His Son, Jesus Christ, died for your sin. As a young man and woman stand before the proper authorities and take each other as husband and wife, so you may stand before the God who made you and say, I ⸻ ⸺, take Thy Son to be my Saviour.

Yes, it is as simple as that when you believe in your heart that Jesus Christ is who God says He is. Do this, and God will immediately give you power to become His child. He will impart to you His very life, and you will experience regeneration, new birth, salvation and God-given life in your innermost being. Then and only then will you know that no amount of sincerity can save, no heathen idol or civilized ritual can give satisfaction, no groping in darkness will lead to light, no other belief can save. In the Bible alone is Christ revealed, and through Christ alone is God revealed. No church, person, creed or penance will do; no giving, paying, doing or praying can avail outside of Christ. He alone is God's Lamb who takes away the sin of the world. You must personally accept Him.

Will you not write your name on the blanks that are provided above? If you do not do this you are really saying, I will not have this Man to reign over me. The truth for which you long, lies just outside the door. Open the door and let Him in.

Biology Texts

SEE THE ACCOMPANYING CHART showing where the teaching concerning the theory of evolution is found in some high school texts. The books analyzed are among the ones most commonly used in the United States. If you study from one of these books, or have access to one to read, you will be interested to look at the suggested pages. They will give you the arguments in various fields, proposed by the evolutionist to account for his theory.

Ten years ago it was a comparatively easy task to compile such a chart, for most of the information about the theory was contained in one chapter. This was usually located near the end of the book. Today, even the revised books by the

WHAT VARIOUS HIGH SCHOOL BIOLOGY TEXTBOOKS TEACH

Textbooks	Similarity as Evidence for Relationship	Evidence from Geology and Paleontology	Change in the Horse	Evidence from Classification
	Pages	Pages	Pages	Pages
Biological Science by W. H. Gregory and E. H. Goldman	707-8	705-6; 710-17	448-49	91-102; 706
Biology by W. J. Kimball	12-16; 543-45	540-43; 581-83		12-18
Biology by C. A. Villee	212; 610-11	592-609	607	92-93; 211-13; 610
Biology by E. Kroeber, W. H. Wolff, R. L. Weaver and D. C. Heath	480-86	460-80; 485	476; 478-99	127-37; 483-84; 486
Biology for You by B. B. Vance and D. F. Miller	524; 534-35	525-35	530	210-11; 531
Design for Life by R. E. Trump and D. L. Fagle	433-38	425-27; 441-44	414-15	431-37; 446-52
Elements of Biology by W. M. Smallwood, I. L. Reveley and G. A. Bailey. Revised by R. A. Dodge	627-34; 661	619-25	623-24	603-16; 627-30
Modern Biology by J. H. Otto and A. Towle	182; 184; 542	182-83; 543-49	522	199-207

same authors, have undergone a radical change. In most of the texts, the largest amount of material is still contained in one chapter. However, scattered throughout the entire book and woven into its very basic framework, one also finds much more of the same teaching. Here and there throughout the books are implications, sentences and paragraphs about this theory. This is generally to the effect that "all reputable scientists" have accepted it as a theory that most facts support and against which there is very little evidence. This book has shown you that the theory has many weaknesses. Existing evidence may be used to support the idea of divine creation as it is revealed to us in the Bible.

Not included in the chart of texts are four high school biology books about which we would say an extra word. These are: *The Science of Biology* by P. B. Weisz; and *Biological Science: An Inquiry Into Life*, Yellow Version; *Biological Science, Molecules to Man*, Blue Version; *High School Biology: BSCS* Green Version.

CONCERNING THE THEORY OF EVOLUTION

Biochemistry	Geographic Distribution	Embryology	Vestigial Structures	Origin of the Universe	Origin of Life	Man	Genetic Cause of Change
Pages	Pages	Pages	Pages	Pages	Pages	Pages	Pages
709-10	450-52; 706-7	708-9	708	9-10	10; 710	464-66; 471-85	721-33
546-48	550-53; 565-91	544-46	545		576-81	612-15	539-40; 548-50; 555-73
611-12	605-6; 615-16	612-14	611		587-89	618-33	575-91; 614-15
453-86	484-86	482-86	483; 486	460	362-64	495-505	488-93
	523-25			525	529; 533	535-40	489-518; 539
442-45	419-25; 445-46	438-40	439-41		45-46	607-21	406-30
	630	625-27	631	618	618-19; 622	266-77	582-99
204; 542	190-97	182-84	182; 184		18-25	542-49	184-90; 193

The last three books were produced by the Biological Science Curriculum Study committee and are usually referred to as the BSCS books. Experts in many fields worked together for a number of years to produce these attractive texts. Many people feel that they are superior to those that a single author could produce and they have been widely adopted by school systems.

The three BSCS books, as well as the one by P. B. Weisz, are so completely evolutionary that it is impossible to analyze them as has been done with the other texts. Not only is organic evolution taken for granted, but it is the very framework of each book. It permeates each text so that no attempt has been made to give the pages on which evidence for the theory is presented.

Bibliography

The fact that the following books are included in the bibliography does not necessarily mean that they express the same opinion as does the author of this book. Rather, a variety of opinions and a diversity of viewpoints are given.

Balyo, J. G. *Creation and Evolution.* Des Plaines, Ill.: Regular Baptist, 1964. Pp. 23. Only a few subjects can be dealt with in these two sermons presented at the Cedar Hills Baptist Church, Cleveland. Spontaneous generation, variation within the biblical "kind," natural selection, creative design and the uniqueness of man are briefly considered.

Biological Sciences Curriculum Study. *Biological Science: An Inquiry into Life.* Yellow Version. New York: Harcourt, Brace & World, 1963. Pp. 748.

———. *Biological Science: Molecules to Man.* Blue Version. Boston: Houghton Mifflin, 1963. Pp. 815.

———. *High School Biology: BSCS Green Version.* Chicago: Rand McNally, 1963. Pp. 749.

Clark, R. E. D. *The Christian Stake in Science.* Chicago: Moody, 1967. Pp. 160. Dr. Clark is an English author. Although this book deals with the origin of the universe, life and early man, it also includes a discussion of the flood and treats many of the physical sciences.

———. *Darwin: Before and After.* Chicago: Moody, 1967. Pp. 192. The growth of the evolutionary theory is traced up to the present time. The creationist view is defended and some of the inconsistencies of the theory of evolution are pointed out.

Coder, S. M., and Howe, G. F. *The Bible, Science and Creation.* Chicago: Moody, 1966. Pp. 128. The first part of this book deals with the inspiration of the Bible and difficult passages. Several chapters are devoted to the Bible's account of origins, the evolutionary theory, fossil man and the time of creation. The last concerns the way archeology and prophecy confirm the veracity of Scripture.

Darwin, Charles. *Origin of Species*. 5th ed., part 2; New York: Random House, 1963. Pp. 1000.

Drake, Francis and Katharine. "Australia's Great Barrier Reef," *Reader's Digest*. Vol. XC, No. 539 (March, 1967), pp. 162-70.

"The Drama of Life Before Birth," *Life* magazine. Vol. LVIII, No. 17 (April 30, 1965), p. 58.

Filby, F. A. *Creation Revealed*. Westwood, N.J.: Revell, 1966. Pp. 160. This book gives a detailed study of Genesis 1. There is a special chapter on the origin of man and one on the Sabbath rest. The author is a creationist who holds the theory that the creative days could have been long periods of time.

Frair, Wayne, and Davis, P. William. *The Case for Creation*. Chicago: Moody, 1967. Pp. 96. A critical examination of some of the theoretical foundations of modern evolution and excursions into specific controversial areas. It is designed to stimulate the development of a biblically sound alternative satisfying to the scientific and intellectual viewpoint.

Goodnight, C. J.; Goodnight, M. L.; and Armacost, R. R. *Biology, An Introduction to the Science of Life*. New York: Wiley, 1962.

Gregory, W. H. and Goldman, E. H. *Biological Science*. Boston: Ginn, 1968. Pp. 920.

Howe, G. F. *God Created*. Chicago: Moody, 1964. Pp. 33. The first of two short chapters deals with the creation of plants and animals, and the second with the creation of man. There is a discussion of some of the fossils of ancient men.

Kerkut, G. A. *Implications of Evolution*. New York: Pergamon, 1960. Pp. 146.

Kimball, J. W. *Biology*. Reading, Mass.: Addison-Wesley, 1965. Pp. 704.

Klotz, J. W. *Genes, Genesis and Evolution*. St. Louis: Concordia, 1955. Pp. 575. This gives the orthodox Lutheran viewpoint. The book includes most of the subjects dealing with evolution and is very useful for both study and reference. It is written in textbook style and has been adapted in some places for classroom use.

———. *Modern Science in the Christian Life.* St. Louis: Concordia, 1961. Pp. 191. This book deals with many subjects besides evolution. Physical as well as biological sciences are considered. It is less technical than some books and therefore better reading for the layman.

Kroeber, E.; Wolff, W. H.; and Weaver, R. L. *Biology.* Boston: Heath, 1960. Pp. 646.

Kylstra, Johannes. "A Mouse Breathes Liquids—and Lives." *Life* magazine. Vol. LXIII, No. 8 (August 25, 1967), p. 78.

Marsh, F. L. *Evolution, Science and Creation.* Washington, D. C.: Review & Herald, 1947. Pp. 381. From the Seventh-Day Adventist position this book deals with most of the subjects usually presented as evidence for the theory of evolution and states how they may be refuted.

Mixter, R. L. *Creation and Evolution.* Monograph Two. Mankato, Minn.: Amer. Scientific Affiliation, 1962 reprint. Pp. 31. This is a discussion of the two topics suggested by the title. It is written for those who have had some background in the sciences. It offers an evaluation of some of the evidences usually presented by the evolutionist. The reasonableness of the position of the creationist is logically shown.

Mixter, R. L. (ed.). *Evolution and Christian Thought Today.* Grand Rapids: Eerdmans, 1959. Pp. 224. This excellent book is a symposium written by thirteen Christian scientists and theologians. The purpose as given in the preface is "to establish the exact import of the theory of evolution; to weigh the claims made by its proponents in the light of contemporary research; to reexamine the Scriptural data relevant to the questions of origin and organic development." A very valuable book.

Morris, H. M. *The Twilight of Evolution.* Philadelphia: Presb. & Ref., 1963. Pp. 103. The supposed evidences in favor of evolution, when closely examined, are seen to be merely shadows. In secular circles, evolution is still taken for granted. The author is a flood geologist who believes evolution is both antibiblical and unscientific.

Morris, H. M., and Whitcomb, S. C. *The Genesis Flood.* Philadelphia: Presb. & Ref., 1961. Pp. 518. This book holds the position that the flood was worldwide and the earth is very young. It points out objections to uniformitarian geology and radioactive dating methods. Although it contains much material with which this author does not agree, it stimulates a person to rethink and restudy many fields.

Otto, J. H., and Towle, A. *Modern Biology.* New York: Holt, Rinehart & Winston, 1965. Pp. 787.

Ramm, Bernard. *The Christian View of Science and the Scripture.* Grand Rapids: Eerdmans, 1954. Pp. 368. This is a thorough, well-documented outline of the problems which confront a harmony of science with Scripture in physics, astronomy, chemistry, zoology and botany. On many debatable issues more than one side of the question is presented.

Shute, E. E. *Flaws in the Theory of Evolution.* Grand Rapids: Baker, 1966. Pp. 286. The title of this book explains the contents. It deals with subjects that are problems to those who accept macroevolution. Biblical creation is upheld, with dates nearer those of the uniformitarian geologist than those of Ussher's chronology.

Smallwood, W. M.; Reveley, I. L.; and Bailey, G. A. *Elements of Biology.* Revised by Ruth A. Dodge. Rockleigh, N. J.: Allyn & Bacon, 1964. Pp. 740.

Snyder, L. H., and David, P. R. *Principles of Heredity.* 4th ed.; Boston: Heath, 1951. Pp. 515.

Stoner, Peter W. *Science Speaks.* Chicago: Moody, 1958 reprint. Pp. 126. The first half of this book deals with the accuracy of the Genesis account of creation. The last is occupied with the definiteness of prophecy stated as a probability.

Trump, R. F., and Fagle, D. L. *Design for Life.* New York: Holt, Rinehart & Winston, 1963. Pp. 664.

Vance, B. B., and Miller, D. F. *Biology for You.* Philadelphia: Lippincott, 1963. Pp. 660.

Villee, C. A. *Biology.* Philadelphia: Saunders, 1967.

Ward, R. R. *In the Beginning.* Grand Rapids: Baker, 1967. Pp. 110. This book contains a series of ten lessons written for young people in order to help them "resist evolutionary philosophy and hold firmly to their faith in God and the Bible." At the end of each chapter are questions and suggested activities.

Weisz, P. B. *The Science of Biology.* New York: McGraw-Hill, 1967. Pp. 786.

Zimmerman, P. A. (ed.). *Darwin, Evolution and Creation.* St. Louis: Concordia, 1963. Pp. 231. The title gives one an idea of the scope of the contents of the book. Six good chapters are written by four different Lutheran scientists. A long bibliography and three indexes increase the usefulness of the book.

Subject Index